To James

Who says insurance is boring?

REFLECTIONS OF A RASCAL

Nigel Kubbler Clarkertln

REFLECTIONS OF A RASCAL

Nigel Kemble-Clarkson

Book Guild Publishing
Sussex, England

First published in Great Britain in 2010 by
The Book Guild Ltd
Pavilion View
19 New Road
Brighton, BN1 1UF

Typesetting in Baskerville by
Norman Tilley Graphics Ltd

Printed in Great Britain by
CPI Antony Rowe

A catalogue record for this book is available from
The British Library

ISBN 978 1 84624 423 0

For Suzie with love.
The one who tamed me.

Contents

1

Going Gay

We're going gay, going gay,
We're going to have a holiday.
So start to laugh and begin to cheer,
The Coronation is drawing near.

We're going gay, going gay,
We'll be so happy on that great day.
So shout out hip hip hooray,
Because we're going, going gay.

These were the opening verses of an extravaganza which was being staged by the Martlet Theatre Group to celebrate Queen Elizabeth II's Coronation. As I watched my mother cavorting with other members of the garishly attired chorus, I cringed with the excruciating embarrassment that only an adolescent can experience.

At 13 years old, I was proud to have been given the job of stage curtain operator and had just performed my new duty to open the show. Much to my relief, despite the cords' unlubricated, rusty pulley wheels, the operation had gone off smoothly.

It was nepotism that had placed me on the bottom rung of Haywards Heath's ladder to amateur dramatic stardom. Although Mother's stage appearances were infrequent, they usually went down well with the locals. However, my saturnine father's sinister portrayals of villains, from Dracula to Captain Hook and Baron Skinflint, had made him a local legend. In fact, around pantomime time, he was often booed and hissed by kids in the High Street. Praise indeed!

Martlet productions were always staged in the town's Public Hall whose draughty Edwardian facilities were decidedly lacking in human comforts. All the shows were directed and sometimes written by Paddy O'Riley, who was a highly strung but very talented Irishman. Although a humble bank clerk by trade, the smell of greasepaint instantly turned him into a thespian fanatic. Although Paddy's direction style was somewhat coercive, his enthusiasm was infectious and inspired results which, though not always perfect, were always entertaining.

The 'Going Gay' review was a compilation of songs, recitations and sketches scheduled for six evening performances plus two matinees. Sadly, my Monday night success was not destined to stay the course.

On Tuesday the slinky Miss Annette Perritt was sorely tested whilst responding to a phone call in her role as a hotel receptionist.

Hello, this is Sloane seven thousand,
The Hotel Magnifique, that's right.
Although you sound smart,
I must say from the start
We have not got a room for tonight.

During my overenthusiastic opening of the curtains, I managed to snap one of the running strings, which left the poor lady spouting the ditty whilst peering round a static shroud. By the time I rescued the situation, subtle humour had degenerated into base farce as her fragile young body strained to shift the hotel desk to the open half of the stage.

Apart from curtain manipulation, I had been allocated certain off-stage acoustical duties which included creating thunder storm effects for a Count Dracula skit. This involved rotating a handle on an ingenious machine which rattled sheets of metal and flicked light bulbs on and off. As the contraption was rather cumbersome, I was supposed to stow it away after use. However, following the second show, I did not bother to do so as it made a convenient seat. The obstruction was to create an upset on Thursday night by crowding the players' entry during a voluminously robed choral slot.

The Borgias are having an orgy,
There's a Borgia orgy tonight.
We've run out of strychnine and that is so sickening,
The gravy will have to have ground glass for thickening.
We've hidden an asp in the iced cantaloupe
And laudanum lurks in the mock turtle soup
So soon all the guests will be looping the loop
At the Borgia orgy tonight.

As the infamous papal family repositioned for the second verse, Rodrigo Borgia suddenly fell flat on his back. He had been pulled over by his long gilded sash which had snagged on the crank handle of my storm simulator. In a moment of inspiration, Lucretia Borgia, who happened to be my mother, saved the situation. With a stage-whispered, 'Stay where you are', she stabbed the Pope with her rubber dagger and the remaining verses were sung over his recumbent form.

As postman Len on the piano accompanied by local farmer Rustic Ron's drums filled in a brief interlude, I was berated by my fiery little Canadian mum.

'You wretched boy. Uncle Paddy has told you to get that thing out of the way a hundred times. Now look what's happened!'

'Leave the lad alone, Roie, he's doing his best. It was my fault for getting entangled and there's no harm done.'

My supporter was the murder victim, Willie Brown, a senior teacher at the local secondary modern school. Heavily in touch with his female side long before such inclinations became fashionable, he was a pantomime dame par excellence. As my mother backed off with her eyes raised to heaven, Willie patted my bottom and removed the offending contraption as I geared up for the next act.

However, misfortune had not deserted me yet and returned with a vengeance on Friday night during Jill Roberts's big moment. She was a tasty blonde with a tastier reputation, whose father was our local dentist. Well-heeled daddy was known as Macavity as, like his daughter's escorts, he rarely failed to find something to fill!

Her number in the show verged on type-casting as she wore a highly revealing, black velvet dress with complementary hosiery and long gloves. Thus attired, she then had to deliver a recitation whilst sitting on a bar stool, orbed and sceptred, holding a cocktail and a long, smoking cigarette holder.

He took me to his rooms to see his etchings
But there was only one I liked the best.
Just an anchor and a chain,
Very simple, very plain,
But most attractive, it was tattooed on his chest.

Unfortunately, the failure of an instant blackout to terminate this risqué recital precipitated my next gaff. As I hurriedly pulled the curtain closing cord to save the situation, the slack tangled with the fabric cocktail bar canopy which collapsed. To hoots of glee from the audience, this knocked Jill off her perch and she was still writhing on the stage with her legs in the air when darkness belatedly restored order.

There are few things in life more destabilising than having one's career threatened, and that is what happened to me following Friday's disaster. Scene shifter Barry Baldwin, a local butcher's boy who worked for the stage manager, Burt Snell, had been coveting the curtain operation job all the week. Following my third hiccup, he made his play. This was done in front of me, with his pimples glistening and his thin lips drawn back in a sneer which revealed two rows of unbrushed yellow teeth.

'Mr Snell, I should have done the curtains like what I done for the panto. Nigel now mucked up three times. It's not fair; I should get a turn tomorrow for the matinee and the last night.'

Feeling ruffled by this invective, I foolishly overreacted. 'You just shut your face, Spotty. Mr Snell, he is just jealous because I am getting all the laughs!'

The butcher's chins wobbled in outraged indignation. 'Well, I think my lad has a point and you are being an awful bighead, Nigel. Just for that I am going to …'

My bacon was saved by the director's intervention. 'Oh, come on, Burt. The boy's got to start somewhere and I am sure that he has learnt by his mistakes like we all have to. I say we let him finish the job.'

4

As Snell waddled off in a huff, followed by a whinging Barry, I felt a twinge of conscience over Paddy's support as I had planned a certain agenda for Saturday night's performance.

Bill 'Stubby' Stamp was a stroppy little quantity surveyor whose leery, unrequited pursuit of the fair sex was a local joke. He was, however, an accomplished theatrical performer, especially when typecast in a part such as the Yellow Dwarf.

As Stubby was a sad bundle of inhibitions and half my size, we were never destined to get the best out of each other. However, due to his lustful designs on Miss Perritt, our antipathy became intensified following my 'Hotel Magnifique' faux pas. He demonstrated this whilst exiting a particularly messy kitchen sketch just before the interval during Wednesday's show.

'Just watch it in future, Nigel.'

On growling these words, Stubby daubed my features with wet dough and strutted off in fits of malevolent laughter. Thinking himself no end of a wag, he unwisely decided to repeat this tedious act on a nightly basis. As war had been declared, I decided to fight fire with fire and so, when I was anointed on Saturday night, I picked the dough off my face, rolled it into a ball and stowed it in my pocket.

Like Willie Brown, Bill Stamp was an adept female impersonator and could sing in a piercingly powerful falsetto voice. The last spot in the programme featured him performing a number, dead pan, dressed in a blonde wig, green feathers and a suitably padded red ball gown.

Follow follow follow the merry merry pipes of Pan,
The magic reed that charms the need of every maid and man.
Ahaha ah away away they seem to say oh catch us if you can,
So follow follow where they lead, theee merry merry pipes of Pan.

The sketch also included my father, Jack, as a garden gnome and Uncle Paddy in a Pan outfit, furry legs, horns, pipes and all. As Stubby warbled, the two of them capered around him making suggestive gestures with a series of garden implements. The climax of the skit was Pan emptying the contents of a watering can into the singer's cleavage during a prolonged holding of the song's final note. The stream of water actually flowed into a sub-neckline funnel and was siphoned off into a bucket behind the scenery. Strangely enough, on the closing night, the rubber piping somehow became blocked.

The little runt's trilling turned into a pained scream as the cold water flowed through his costume, soaking him to the skin. The audience lapped up every moment and their laughter and applause barely faltered when the deluge short-circuited the footlights. The finale, which was illuminated by some surviving spotlights, received a standing ovation and the review was hailed as Paddy's greatest triumph to date.

Although some vicious rumours were bandied about, the presence of a piece of dough in the relief conduit was to remain a mystery!

As Christmas approached, members of the Martlet Theatre Group were eagerly girding their artistic loins in preparation for the annual pantomime. After deep deliberation, the committee decided to grace Haywards Heath's theatre-goers with a production of *Jack and the Beanstalk*. This delighted Father, as it meant that he would be portraying his favourite rotter, Baron Skinflint. In view of her busy social calendar, Mother was sidelined to a minor role as Flavia, an 'immortal' in the giant's cloudy kingdom.

Now that I had achieved the great age of 14, I was considered ripe for my initiation into treading the boards. Although this was probably really due to the group members wanting to keep me away from 'props' at all costs, I did not care: I had arrived. The bad news was that my debut was to be performed inside a cow suit; the good news was that I was to play the front half with Barry Baldwin occupying the rear end. The risk of his smearing anti pustule balm on the seat of my trousers was compensated for by my intention to be on a baked bean diet for the week of the show!

As it turned out, due to some mix-up with Drury's, the Brighton costumiers, there were no cow outfits available. Ever flexible, Paddy did a swift script rewrite and transformed Barry and me into Hacker the horse; probably the only one of its species whose farts implode!

It was around this time, somewhat late by today's standards, that I started to take a keen interest in the opposite sex. This gave a whole new dimension to the communal dressing room where the entire cast got changed. Of course, all the chaps were terribly British when using this open facility and would avert their gaze from female players' involuntary exposures. I have to admit, however, that my chivalry was applied selectively and it was in this open environment that I fell madly in lust with Jack, the 'principal boy'.

The part was being played by Penny Pritchard, a local 19-year-old lass whose daddy was reputedly the youngest brigadier in the British Army. Having been initially attracted by her sparkling, piquant features, it was the regular sightings of her voluptuous body that really got my hormones jangling. I shall never forget the thrill of glimpsing the soft shadow of her lush cupid's mount which was temptingly visible through her translucent panties.

Not surprisingly, my wide-eyed loitering in the changing room soon aroused attention, and it was Father who was first to intervene.

'Nigel, it does not take half an hour to don your horse trousers and pick up your nag's head. Stop mooning around gawping at the ladies and go and read a book or have a game of cards in the coffee room. That goes for you too, Barry.'

My hindquarters unwisely decided to react aggressively. 'You can't tell me what to do Mr Kemble-Clarkson; I don't like playing cards and reading is for toffs, so there.'

Father regarded Barry with his dangerous, humourless smile. 'Then why not go and count your spots? That should keep you occupied for some time.'

As I led the boy away before he could dig himself a deeper grave, he turned to me and whined, 'That's not fair, and it's all your fault for staring at Miss Pritchard.'

He was perfectly correct, of course, but he was still a moron so far as I was concerned.

This altercation occurred prior to Sunday's final dress rehearsal and created a timely interlude, during which I was to enhance my role. As Barry had foolishly decided to sulk in the auditorium, his leisure was soon forestalled when Bert Snell drafted him into some scene-shifting duties.

Meanwhile, whilst I was sitting alone in the recreation room, staring aimlessly into my horse's head, I made a discovery. Tucked up in the skull's interior were a number of coiled strings with wooden toggles. Pulling away some old insulation tape which held them in place, I discovered that their manipulation brought the bland equestrian visage to life. Four cords controlled separate eye-rolling and ear-flapping whilst another one opened the sprung toothy mouth. I decided not to reveal my discovery until the first night, when I could give everyone a pleasant surprise. However, urgent necessity was to bring this event forward.

So far, Hacker the horse had only taken part in three on-stage rehearsals. These had been a disaster as, due to the highly limited vision via mesh windows in his neck and belly, Barry and I had totally failed to navigate him. Paddy had been obliged to guide us into our allotted positions and, the weekend before, he had flown into one of his Gallic rages.

'You are both a bloody shambles, particularly you, Nigel, as the front runner. Barry, as and when he heads in the right direction, all you have to do is follow his feet and stop when he stops, not keep shunting him and wandering off sideways. There is free space in the hall all the week so get together in the evenings and *practice, practice, practice*, until you get it right. Is that *clear*?'

We had both agreed with alacrity but, as the two of us were not destined to be natural collaborators, our good intentions fell on stony ground. The one attempt we made to rehearse was a complete disaster when, due to our continued arguing, our 'dresser' Rick got fed up and went off to the pub. This left us to disentangle ourselves from the straps of the enveloping costume unaided, which simply exacerbated our animosity.

And so, as we stumbled from the wings the following Sunday afternoon, we were still ill-prepared to meet the demands of our role. Our first scene involved the build-up to Jack's sale of the beloved family horse for a handful of magic beans. With my gangling body crouched forward, the restricted view made the top of the principal boy's tights a focal point. The distraction induced me to veer too closely to the stage's edge which caused Barry to catch his hoof on a footlight and fall into the small orchestra pit. Chaos reigned as Penny and other cast members grabbed my mane to prevent me following my arse into a scattered heap of drums and cymbals.

Rustic Ron was bellowing obscenities as he tried to rescue his instruments, whilst Barry wailed and Paddy uttered dire threats. His invective then focused on me when he discovered that Penny's laughter was being echoed from inside the horse's head. Had I then been aware of the maxim that, if you laugh with a woman you are halfway to her bedroom, I might have weathered the ensuing diatribe with greater fortitude.

The director was beside himself with rage as Barry and I, now separated and partly peeled, stood trembling before him.

'You two are a pathetic disgrace and could ruin the entire show. I am going to deem this scene completed and, as you are not due on again for another half an hour or so, you will re-don your costume and practice at the back of the auditorium. If you are then not up to scratch for the beanstalk ascension scene and your other slots thereafter, I shall write Hacker out of the script altogether.

'Now *move it* and let's get this show back on the road, everyone, *please.*'

Whether or not Paddy could have carried out his threat so late in the day is open to question but, as it turned out, this drastic step proved unnecessary. There is nothing like a bit of pressure to unite the most diverse of spirits so, for the first time, Barry and I worked hard to get it together.

Our next scene was just before the interval. As the stage is gradually dominated by the beanstalk, the evil gypsy Tealeaf, played by Stubby Stamp, rushes on dragging Hacker behind him. He then tries to demand full rights to the prolific vegetable for returning the horse, and is driven off by the villagers. At this, Jack parades with his cherished beast as the entire cast dances around them, bidding him a lusty Godspeed. The first half closes as the hero climbs up the swollen tendrils waving an enchanted axe, which has been given to him by the Fairy Queen.

> *Happy days are here again,*
> *The evil giant will soon be slain*
> *Then our village will be free from pain,*
> *Happy days are here again.*
> *[Etc ...]*

The chorus was dominated by pimply adolescent girls from the Vera Clegg School of Dancing. Old Vera was a scrawny, lantern-jawed spinster with a heart of gold whose screeching directions did little to coordinate the tottering gyrations of her pupils. Sadly, her troupe did not possess a deodorant stick between them. This meant that, although personal hygiene was far more relaxed in those days, the nostrils of other cast members were still sorely put to the test. Indeed, Hacker's musty interior provided a welcome escape from the tangy, onion-like fumes which pervaded the stage during the girls' more energetic dances.

However, Barry and I had responded miraculously well to Paddy's pressure and managed to move faultlessly about the stage, with me nuzzling Jack whenever I got the chance. As is ever my wont, success made me grossly overconfident and I went right over the top by attempting a few dance steps. This completely threw my rear end out of gear which brought forth a fresh tirade of abuse from Paddy so, as it was now face-saving time, I decided to play my trump card.

As Jack commenced his ascent, I grabbed the toggles suspended in front of me and indulged in some puppeteering. When Hacker suddenly extended his personality, the performance came to a halt as everyone dissolved into fits of laughter. The horse's rolling eyes, twitching ears and gnashing smile had taken everyone by surprise, not least of our director, who was patently impressed.

'Well, that is bloody brilliant, Nigel. It gives a whole new dimension to the role that you two were about to make redundant. When Jack gets control of her giggles, maybe she would be kind enough to resume her Giant cull mission before any more villagers are eaten.'

So the week of the show unfolded smoothly with Hacker's participation extended to include an unlikely visit to the Giant's kitchen. We were also brought into the pre-finale kiddies' interlude. This is where Jack and the comic, Billy Muggins (played by Paddy), display an inevitable community song on placards and drill it into the ever-eager audience.

> *How high does a fly fly when a fly flies ever so high?*
> *We know a bird flies to its nest,*
> *We know a cold flies to the chest.*
> *We know where the flies go when the wintry weather is nigh,*
> *But how high does a fly fly when a fly flies ever so high?*

> *Old Mother Riley,*
> *Queen of all the fairies.*
> *Bung it in the basket,*
> *Thurp [raspberry], hold that.*

What these lyrics lacked in refinement was certainly compensated for by originality and, during the audience's indoctrination, children were invited up onto the stage. Here, they would meet Hacker and then play some silly games with Jack and Billy. One of them involved me stamping my front hoof to correspond with the fingers that a child held up behind me. The number of stomps required was transmitted via subtle hand signals from Jack in front of my netting window. Sadly, this seemingly harmless game was destined to cause me considerable grief.

Whilst Hacker's fortunes blossomed to such a degree that my

partner in skin and I were becoming quite pally, my romantic ambitions were going nowhere. As Baron Skinflint had curtailed my ornithological observations in the changing room, the only time that I got close to Ms Pritchard was on stage. As on such occasions she was ever coquettish, my aspirational torch was being cruelly kept aflame.

Unfortunately, the main barrier to my affections was none other than the Giant himself in the form of Ralph Clutton. Ralph was a young City stockbroker whose rugged good looks towered over my bony 6-foot frame. He had made a name for himself in the 'Going Gay' production and, with his head stuck inside a vast papier mâché gargoyle, he portrayed an adequate titan. His adulation of Penny was painfully obvious, and he had already swatted me like a fly after the show one night when I was hanging out with Barry.

'If you two wish to swig beer in the park after hours, don't do it whilst walking behind Miss Pritchard and I. Particularly you, Nigel. I find it extremely irritating the way that you are always hanging around the wings gawping like a cat. I am sure that you would not really want to get my goat, now would you?'

I restrained Barry from saying something crass as we moved off into the chill, misty lamplight to finish our brown ales. This put down called for a more furtive response.

Fee fai fo fum, I smell the ... aachoo ... b-blood of an Englishoo. Whether he be alive or whether he be de ... dea ... dead ... tishoo. I'll grind his bones to make my breshoo ... bread.

This was how the Giant's opening speech came across during the Friday evening performance.

'Dear me, Barry,' I remarked. 'Poor old Ralph seems to have caught a nasty cold.'

'It must be all that wandering about in Victoria Park with his girlfriend. He should keep his trousers on,' my new friend responded with uncharacteristic aplomb.

In accordance with theatrical tradition, no accusations were made concerning a quantity of pepper discovered in the Giant's false head, but suspicion was rife!

On Saturday the matinee went off remarkably well and everyone in the company was raring to go for the final night's performance. Unfortunately this heralded the fateful moment that any hopes I nurtured of getting closer to Penny were dashed. Everything was fine until the community song interlude when an exceptionally short little girl was selected to test Hacker's numeracy. In order to ascertain the tot's digital signals and pass them on to me, Jack got too close to Hacker's front end. The result was that my stamping hoof descended upon her foot, causing a heart-rending shriek of pain. Thinking that this was all part of the show, the audience loved it as Penny hopped about the stage in agony until a blackout was imposed.

Although our intrepid 'principal boy' managed to hobble through the finale, it was patently obvious that she was severely injured. I was, therefore, somewhat daunted when, as she was being bandaged by Vera Clegg afterwards, I found myself in the shadow of Ralph's bulky form. To my surprise his craggy face bore the shadow of a smile.

'Don't feel too badly about it old lad; you have done a great job all week and accidents will happen. While your father is not looking, do have a gin and orange to warm you up for the last-night beano.'

As I was very thirsty following my stuffy confinement, I grabbed the proffered glass and emptied it in one rippling gulp.

'Wow,' exclaimed my corrupter in feigned admiration. 'An accomplished drinker too. Let me get you another.'

I was of course being set up, but as my day-to-day experience of hard liquor was smelling it on grown-ups' breath, I failed to realise it. This was until, having downed a second drink, I was on my way to the loo when a wave of dizziness obliged me to steady myself on the furniture. Having done some deep breathing whilst I was on the can, I left the hall via the stage door and, following a brisk walk in the cold night air, felt much recovered.

On my return I wolfed down a couple of egg sandwiches as I joined everyone in the newly cleared auditorium for the get-together. As Len and Ron put our hit parade recognition skills to the test, Stubby bounded up to me wielding a bottle of Scotch.

'Nigel, the best-looking horse in the stables. As it is officially still the festive season, how about burying the hatchet and having a wee dram with your old sparring partner?'

With this, he filled two paper cups with the amber liquid and passed one to me. 'OK, young fellow, down the hatch in one go.'

Although I realised that accepting a gift from an enemy was probably a mistake, I did rather enjoy the warm glow that swept over me as I finished the whisky.

'Thanks, Stubby. You really are not such a bad chap after all.'

'It's Mr Stamp to you, young fellow,' was growled up at me as the manikin turned and stomped off in a huff.

I could not have cared less that my relationship with Stubby was back in the mire, as my priority was to make an important apology. Whilst the rural minstrels murdered a popular Charleston revival number, I weaved my way across to where Penny and Ralph were sitting. Trying to ignore an uncomfortable tightening in my throat, I gave a caressing pat to the bandaged limb which was resting on a stool.

'May I say that, if your foot is broken, then so is my heart and …'

My impassioned speech was cut short by another 'Ralph' and his close partner 'Hugheee'! Having projected vomit all over the horrified couple, I was ignominiously led away by my livid mother like the errant schoolboy that I had certainly shown myself to be.

Amazingly, my shameful conduct did not mark the end of my involvement with the group, thus precipitating a situation which led to a far more outrageous scenario a year later.

If the trials and tribulations of being confined within a musty horse outfit had been exacting, they was nothing compared to the demands of my role the following year. However, in view of my *Jack and the Beanstalk* gaff, acceptance of this part was probably the only reason why my featuring in a Martlet production was still tolerated. Who else in their right mind would agree to being coated all over with black greasepaint and then go on stage in just underpants, a raffia skirt and a curly wig? This is exactly what I had to do for seven performances when I was cast as Man Friday in the company's production of *Robinson Crusoe*.

The silver lining of this dark cloud which proved to be my path to disaster was that Judy Burrage, a delectable 22-year-old, had been chosen to play the title role. This auburn-haired, green-eyed goddess was a member of one of the few local Irish families and, like Kerry her mother, was notorious for her romantic escapades. Judy's sudden interest in amateur dramatics was undoubtedly to escape from her rich but deadly dull husband.

Bertie Burrage worked for his rough-diamond father, Stan, who was making a fortune replacing the lush meadowland between Redhill and Brighton with ugly red brick dormitories. In spite of an expensive education, he displayed none of his dad's canny acumen and was generally regarded as a feckless popinjay. When not enjoying long lunches with friends, Bertie's contribution to the firm was relaxing with his feet on his desk, as he chain-smoked and sipped the odd pink gin.

So far I had been obliged to worship Judy from afar whilst she cavorted with Harris-Tweeded Young Conservatives in the local cafes and pubs. However, now that my Man Friday role dictated close proximity, this magnificent siren was to fan the smouldering fuse of my sexual awakening to detonation point. The satanic horns which goaded us along this inevitable path were humour and physical contact, for which our thespian relationship had been perfectly scripted.

A prime example of the staged humorous moments occurs during our first encounter when I creep out from behind some ferns and stalk the desert island's new arrival.

Very soon, Crusoe, looking gorgeous in a skimpy fur top, skin-tight knee britches and leather boots, realises that he is not alone. However, as every time he turns round I dive for cover, some help from the audience is inspired.

'Please, dear girls and boys, I have a creepy feeling that I am being followed, if you see someone, could you shout out and let me know?'

As I then make a fleeting appearance, the younger theatre goers erupt in top-decibel excitement.

'Look round now! He's behind you!'

I continue my ducking and diving.

'Oh no he isn't.'

'Oh yes he is. There he goes again!'

After a few minutes of traditional pantomime lore, I am, of course, discovered and bundled to the front of the stage by slender, well-manicured hands.

'Oolah hoolah boyo. Glucker luperfitter.'

These are my opening lines, followed by similar gibberish as Robinson desperately tries to communicate with me. Fortunately, this gave me the opportunity to titillate Judy's bubbling sense of humour via affecting absurd variations to my meaningless dialogue. Having played it straight at rehearsals and on the first night, my Tuesday greeting switched to:

'Roley howler bowow. Glitter pintabitter.'

Thereafter, I invented different lines for each performance, opening on Saturday evening with: 'Randy gluta bangbang. Graba winternicker.'

Thus, every night when this scene had ended, Judy and I would fall into each other's arms as our repressed giggles exploded into convulsions of mirth. All the while I was desperately trying to convince myself that humour really might be an aphrodisiac.

Paddy's story line was an eclectic hotchpotch which included characters out of *Treasure Island* and *Peter Pan*. Thus, at one stage, due to Captain Hook corrupting some natives, Crusoe and I are cast into a cooking pot next to Ben Gun and Captain Van Nish. At each performance, I silently thanked Burt Snell for the economy of space in the canvas receptacle as I squeezed in beside Judy. It was during the delightful five minutes prior to our rescue by Tiger Lily that Judy made her first accidental intimate contact. This was on Tuesday, and was to be inadvertently repeated on a nightly basis! However, it was not to be until Saturday night that my romantic aspirations were more meaningfully rewarded.

As I assumed that my flirtations with Judy during the course of the week were not destined to lead anywhere, events which occurred after the finale took me completely by surprise.

With a successful and profitable week's run completed, an atmosphere of euphoria pervaded the dressing room as everyone prepared for the closing party.

Mother, who was there for the celebrations, irritatingly took over the removal of my native hue, where the principal boy had often been so helpful. However, I eventually escaped her to complete

cleaning up in the washroom and it was here that my introduction to the wicked ways of the female sex took place.

Just as I had completed scrubbing my face in a cracked, mottled mirror, Judy slid into the anteroom and closed the door behind her. As she was clad in only a bra and panties, my instant reaction was one of combined awe and elation, mainly focused in the pit of my stomach, or thereabouts!

'Hi, Robinson. Great show, eh? Well done. Could you check that I have got all the muck off my face, I believe that ...'

Before I knew it, I had been drawn into my very first grown-up embrace. Although I had shared the odd adolescent kiss at country dances, the thrill of an exploratory expert at work with tongue and finger tips had so far eluded me. Immediately warming to the experience, I was optimistically wondering if there was room in the adjacent lavatory to progress matters, when the main door strained against my back.

'Make way for a desperate man, my first pint has gone straight through me.'

Much to my relief, the intruder was Uncle Paddy who, as a

renowned lecher, was surely not likely to be offended. The scowl on his face instantly indicated that my assumption was incorrect.

'Good God, what the hell are you two up to? Judy, you are a married woman and he is underage. This is a total disgrace!'

Attired as she was, Judy was in no position to stand on her dignity, but, grabbing a towel for partial cover, she did her best.

'How dare you suggest impropriety, I was assisting the boy to remove the last of his make-up. Just because you fancy yourself as the local Casanova, don't apply your standards to others. If you do not apologise instantly, I shall report your insulting remarks to Bertie.'

Our accuser was taken aback by Judy's aggressive stance and wisely decided to back down.

'I really do not believe that you will mention anything of the sort to your husband, my dear. However, it would be a shame to spoil the party, so why don't we allay any suspicions by walking out of here together? Let's have no more of this nonsense. And Nigel, kindly adjust those ridiculous black underpants.'

One might have thought that this altercation would have cooled my ardour but, like a shark that has scented blood, I was not going to give up easily.

Once auditorium chairs had been stacked, everyone who was in any way connected with the pantomime assembled for the traditional soirée. Unfortunately, this meant that my antics during the course of the evening were witnessed by a broad spectrum of the local hoi polloi.

As my parents were ballroom dance enthusiasts, they had ensured that, even at my young age, I was reasonably capable of tripping the light fantastic. These skills had been broadened during the summer whilst staying in London with a school pal whose elder brother introduced us to Humphrey Littleton's Piccadilly Jazz Club. Thus, though not yet that adept at social skills, I was able to impress the opposite sex with my energetic jive and Charleston routines. As for this year's party Len and Ron's services had been replaced by popular gramophone records, there was much more opportunity to show off.

Ever physical, Judy was an accomplished rhythmic mover, so she happily allowed me to monopolise her time on the dance floor. Bertie weirdly encouraged the situation by staying put in his chair and feeding us gin and vermouth during our occasional pauses for breath. Even when his spouse and I emulated Siamese twins during the slower numbers, he appeared to be relaxed as he sipped cocktails and chewed his cane cigarette holder.

In spite of the fact that Judy and I were behaving inappropriately, most of the other partygoers were too preoccupied with their own tipsy pursuits to pay us any heed. Thankfully, this included my parents, and our only interruptions came from Paddy, who kept pointedly insisting that I should dance with my mother. I naturally resisted this pressure but, eventually, it was our revered director who halted the dancing.

Unbeknown to me and most people present, the show's last night happened to coincide with Mrs Burrage's twenty-third birthday. It was only when, to everyone's initial consternation, Len and Ron took up their dreaded instruments to play 'Happy Birthday to You' that all was revealed. With his customary aplomb, Paddy delivered an appropriately light-hearted monologue and, after much applause, presented his 'principal boy' with a bottle of champagne.

To this very day I cannot think what possessed me, but it was at this moment that I committed the faux pas which was to end my fledgling acting career. Whilst Judy still held the floor, following a sweet little speech of thanks, I stepped up to her and took her in my arms.

'My gift to you is my undying love and devotion!'

Having uttered this dramatically corny sentiment, I delivered a lingering kiss that would have earned any film a ban from the Lord Chancellor at the time. To make matters worse, the object of my untimely affection responded with alacrity!

When we eventually disengaged from our clinch, the assembled throng erupted vociferously, expressing views ranging from bawdy approval to indignant outrage. Meanwhile, as Father set about created a diversion by getting the dreaded musical duo to play the 'Hokey Cokey', Mother demonstrated uncharacteristic diplomacy. Grabbing the bull firmly by the horns, she walked straight up to the object of my ardour who was adjusting her make-up.

'Judy. Happy birthday, my love. I thought that you were terrific in the panto. Jack and I are off to Paddy and Muriel's with some of the others to play poker; why don't you and Bertie come along too?'

Before the couple could respond, mother turned to me with murder lurking behind her smile.

'As for you, my lad, I am organising a taxi to take you home. It really is getting far too late for you to be up, especially as you are back to school at the end of next week and you still have not done your prep, you naughty boy.'

At this point the Burrages enthusiastically accepted the card party invitation whilst I was led away, much chastened.

Further revelations do not significantly add to this tale but, at the time, Haywards Heath was rewarded with a scandal which rumbled on until the spring.

The grand irony of the situation had been telegraphed via the director's unexpected disapproval during the washroom incident and again on the dance floor. Although I was not made aware of it at the time, roughly six months after my indiscretions, Paddy and Judy had a torrid affair. Its intensity was such that it almost destroyed the ten-year O'Riley marriage and, when it ended in tears, Judy disappeared to London, leaving Bertie to be comforted by his many male friends.

I had completed my Army service before my dear mother posed the obvious question concerning my relationship with Judy. I lied, whilst Dracula, Captain Hook and Baron Skinflint drew their own conclusions!

2

A Jibe Too Far

Britain's much revered armed services are presently comprised of valiant volunteers who have chosen to pursue this often hazardous career path. Recruitment was not always thus, as at the end of the Second World War the mandatory enlistment system was perpetuated via the National Service Act. As a result of this I joined the echelons of men who, between 1945 and 1961, were assigned to support the 'regulars' for a minimum period of two years.

I sincerely believe that, like me, a vast majority of National Servicemen look back on their period in uniform with fond memories. Not only did we learn to mix with every facet of the British social structure, but also, through training and sport, many of us returned to civilian life in the peak of fitness.

Over the years there have been many books, films and TV programmes covering conscription and its effect on the individuals caught in its web. These depictions, particularly the humourous ones, usually feature the Army, to which a majority of draftees were allocated. Indeed, it was to a unit of this branch of the services that I found myself heading in the back of an ill-sprung lorry one wet autumn morning in 1958.

The last sacrificial lamb to clamber over the vehicle's tailboard at Chichester Station was a vague acquaintance of mine, Peter Stephens. The lad was something of an upper-bracket hooligan who haled from the Plumpton area of Sussex. Our last meeting had been at a country house party where he got himself evicted for pouring five bottles of champagne into a Bechstein grand piano. His addled excuse had been that he thought it was a punchbowl, which did not sit well with his father when he was obliged to cough up £3,000 to repair the damage.

Peter was patently relieved to encounter a familiar face and, true to his crass form, blindly trampled and barged his way through the crowded transport to where I sat. Not surprisingly, by the time he eventually squeezed in beside me on my metal bench, he had failed to impress many of our already disgruntled fellow draftees.

'Nige, great to see you again. Got gaffed and netted too, eh?'

His plummy voice instantly served as an additional irritant to the assembled company, with whom we were both destined to share our lives for the next two and a half months.

'Hi, Peter. I would be able to face privation more philosophically if you removed your bloody suitcase from my foot and stopped sitting all over me.'

The gormless features took on an injured look. 'I say, I am most terribly sorry, old bean, but this thing is hardly a Rolls-Royce, is it? The cattle on Daddy's estate travel in better style than this.'

A voice from the tangled mob around us rang out in a broad Sussex accent: 'F***ing hell. Jolly hockey sticks!'

There was a general raucous peel of laughter and that was it: for the rest of his brief, inglorious military career, Peter was to be known as 'Hockey'.

Our transport eventually came to a grinding halt and, as we were received into a khaki reception committee, the shouting started which was to be part of our immediate existence. However, our military baptism did encompass some palpable good news.

Compared to the crude 'hut and stove' accommodation being allocated to most recruits at this time, Chichester's Rousillon Barracks was a five-star hotel. Having dropped off our meagre luggage, we were marched to the Quartermaster's stores for kitting out before being settled into a brick-built, centrally heated paradise.

The plethora of newly issued equipment included two pairs of heavy-duty, metal-studded boots. These emblems of our new calling were fashioned in coarse leather, and a primary phase of our military initiation was learning how to smooth out their blemished surfaces. To instruct us in this vital art was the incongruously maternal Corporal Chance, a bespectacled Jewish lawyer from Worthing who was also a draft victim. In the mode of a Blue Peter presenter he patiently demonstrated how, with the aid of a lighted candle, two tins of polish and a duster, gleaming results could be achieved. The fact that lengthy exposure to a naked flame was bound to impair the durability of the footwear appeared to be of secondary importance. This was the Army, and ours was not to reason why!

I was soon to discover that the 'icing on the cake' of the military experience was the acerbic humour which flowed from the lips of those charged with instilling discipline. I am, of course, referring to the non-commissioned officer (NCO) cadre. These stalwart gentlemen were far funnier and less invasive than has since been depicted on TV programmes such as *Bad Lad's Army*. With fluid spontaneity, many of them could deliver bawdy repartee with the style and expertise of an Edwardian stand-up music hall comic.

After a dauntingly confusing first day, we eventually retired to our wire-sprung pallets, only to be crudely awakened at 6 a.m. the following morning by the Geordie Corporal Bellas.

'Hands off cocks, on socks. Come on you sleeping beauties, let's have you. I was in Baghdad before you were in dad's bag!'

However swiftly we responded to our wake-up call, achieving breakfast and ablutions plus cleaning our living quarters and kit in the time allocated was an onerous challenge. Thus, our first 7 a.m. muster parade was a total shambles as most of us arrived late, with stomachs rumbling having missed visiting the distant mess hall.

Whilst pacing the ranks after order had been restored, the odorous Corporal Crean observed that pimply Private Samways had managed avoid the previous day's neo-Mohican haircut. He stomped up behind the shaggy rebel with his red, pockmarked face contorted in mock fury.

'Am I hurting you, lad?'

'No, Corp,' was the reply.

'Well I should be, I am standing on your f***ing hair! If you appear on parade in this state again, I will personally groom you with a blowtorch. And it's "Corporal" to you in future.'

As we were now part of a killing machine, not surprisingly a training priority was learning how to handle firearms and unfriendly explosive devices. Although my spell of service saw the phasing in of the Belgian FN automatic rifle, I was destined to rely on a more nostalgic arm. The Lee Enfield Mk IV 303 rifle varied little from the

Mk I version used by our forefathers in the Boer War. This stalwart bolt action gun, which kicked like a mule when fired, could get off a maximum of eight rounds before the magazine had to be manually recharged. Basic, reliable and tough, the weapon was accurate up to 400 yards and sufficiently heavy that, if all else failed, one could bludgeon one's adversaries into submission.

'If this weapon has subdued the enemies of six British monarchs, it should be good enough for you arseholes,' Sergeant Brewer, the corpulent, florid armourer confided, before adding some personal advice. 'You will treat it with even greater respect than you do your God given gun. That one f***s you into trouble; this one gets you out of trouble and ensures someone else stays f***ed!'

Much of our earlier training was marching and rifle drill which offered the perfect setting for the NCOs to demonstrate their verbal abuse skills. This is where, due to his ingenuous foolhardiness, Hockey Stephens managed to offer himself as a perfect victim.

His obstructive conduct had been triggered when the depot CO, Major Newton, told him that his dearth of O levels rendered him ineligible for officer candidature.

'I am buggered if I am going to be pushed about by a bunch of peasants for two years, so I shall prove that I am not cut out to be a common soldier,' Stephens had privately ranted to me.

This was a highly flawed course, but nothing I could say would convince him of his folly. However, although his eccentric behaviour made him an NCOs' butt, it did turn him into an unlikely hero of the rank and file. Hardly a day went by without Hockey being obliged to lap the parade ground perimeter at the double with his rifle held above his head. However, whilst his rebellious career afforded him common popularity, these punishment sessions were to become progressively more draconian.

A primary persecutor of my misguided friend was the excessively moustachioed Sergeant Fawcett, who delighted in pulling him out of the ranks for personal tuition. As this highly anal, bawdy instructor – a keen biker when off duty – had a voice like a bell, these sessions often became a sideshow of colourful invective.

'Stephens, I find your slouching offensive, boy. In fact, I want to see you standing so rigidly to attention that your arsehole goes half-a-crown sixpence, half-a-crown sixpence.'

This type of remark would then be followed up along similar lines: 'If you don't raise your knees when you turn, you will give your arsehole a black eye. As we all know, the remedy for that is raw meat so whilst I administer the treatment, you can shout out the time like you do on parade, so that we get it together. Is that clear?'

Nevertheless Hockey Stephens did not suffer alone as we all received our fair share of abuse.

One of the most original jibes that I managed to inspire was from the lugubrious Company Sergeant Major Thomas. Following some rare weekend leave, I was feeling particularly jaded at Monday's muster inspection, when he gloweringly stamped to a halt in front of me.

'I neither care nor wish to know where you have been or what you may have done over the weekend, but you look and smell like a bucketful of heaving testicles!'

Hand grenade priming and throwing was undoubtedly the most hazardous part of our training programme. In spite of this, scant confidence was instilled by skinny little Sergeant Roper's over-relaxed style of instruction. Apart from the fact that his countenance was worryingly seamed with livid scars, he would nonchalantly compare this dangerous item of weaponry to confectionery.

'The reason for the criss-cross grooves on the casing of this sweet little explosive egg is one of pure generosity. Just as with a bar of chocolate, they ensure that everyone gets a bit.'

Apart from a short-cut time fuse, the main risk whilst practising this skill was that a panicking squaddy might hurl his trigger pin at the 'enemy' and retain the live grenade. On such occasions, all those present had but a few seconds to dive for cover behind the 'wanker's wall' before detonation!

One of my fellow recruits was Nick Burk who, as a result of being a builders' hod carrier by trade, was built like the proverbial brick shithouse. Although he was slightly shorter than my gangling frame, I had been somewhat dismayed on being 'volunteered' to face him in the first session of compulsory boxing. I was soon seeing stars as Nick's milling, sledgehammer blows put me on the canvas three times in as many minutes. However, as I was slightly quicker and much fitter than my opponent, I just about managed to win on points. In spite of the fact that we withdrew from the ring looking like battle casualties, for the rest of the course we were the best of friends. However, like many of us, my new pal was not quite the hard man that he liked to portray. A factor which was to be dramatically demonstrated.

Sergeant Metcalf, our platoon sergeant, acted as a kind of autocratic military nursemaid during our basic training. A compact package of clockwork brawn, I will ever fondly remember him as the personification of a typical British NCO. At the slightest opportunity, he loved to tell people about his impressive display of medal ribbons which always ended with the same quip: 'This is my favourite gong which I won in 1944 as a reward for having been ambushed three times and only shitting myself twice!'

Most probably because I lacked a regional accent and wore a potential officer's red armband, Metcalf put me in charge of the 'shit, shave, shower and shampoo' area. This meant that I had to ensure that the latrines and ablutions were in pristine condition first thing every morning. As this was obviously intended to deliberately put me to the test, I was all the more determined to perform the unsavoury task faultlessly. This often necessitated my having to drag fellow recruits out of the stalls in mid-dump so that I could brush out unmilitary stains from the pans in time for room inspection. As I had been allocated two other squaddies to assist me in these duties, the sergeant surprised me one morning with a back-handed compliment.

'In the unlikely event that I ever have to suffer the humiliation of saluting you, we will both fondly remember "the palace"; your first successful command.'

However, even pillars of the British Army can get rattled and this happened at muster parade one morning when Sergeant Metcalf stopped in front of Nick Burk with a fearsome scowl on his face.

'Your belt is loose, your brasses are crap, your uniform is as crumpled as a whore's undersheet and, as usual, you are a f***ing shambles. In fact I reckon that the best part of you ran down your mother's leg!'

For some reason, this remark somehow seemed to hang in the air so, as I was standing near to my friend in the front rank, I stole a glance at him. Much to my amazement, he was not only eyeballing his tormentor instead of looking straight ahead, but also he was weeping.

An obviously shocked Sergeant Metcalf looked up at the bristling human mountain towering over him and, in a very un-parade-ground voice, said, 'No need to take on so lad. What's the matter?'

Burk replied passionately through his teeth, 'I love my mum, Sarge.'

The Sergeant stepped back a pace and, in almost conciliatory tones, responded, 'All love our mothers, Burk, all love our mothers. Just an Army term of phrase lad, just a term of phrase.'

Sticking his bull head forward for emphasis, Burk reaffirmed at the top of his lungs, 'But I love my mum!'

For just a split second too long, Sergeant Metcalf had lost the initiative and the unthinkable happened. I and every one else on parade subsided into fits of laughter. Then lightning struck.

'Squad! Port arms. Squad will move to the right in threes, right turn. Double march.'

An hour later the furious Sergeant had thoroughly sweated our mutinous conduct out of us, but, in the remaining weeks of training, I never heard him use his 'term of phrase' again.

And so it came to pass that, on a chilly parade ground one morning in Sussex, a hero of El Alamein and the Normandy landings met his Waterloo at the hands of a yokel 'brick monkey'.

3

Almost Decommissioned

The lounge bar of Brighton's Sussex Hotel was crammed with the regular Saturday-night throng of pseudo-Bohemians and their full skirted, painted escorts. Generally known as 'The Crowd', all those present had been friends of mine since long before I was gobbled up by Her Majesty's conscription machine. As this event led to a lengthy overseas posting, I had decided to visit my old haunt in order to say farewell to everyone before my departure.

It was late into an evening of drinks, cuddles and reminiscences when, on glancing into the adjacent saloon bar, I received a shock. Through the dimly lit eddies of tobacco smoke, I observed Messrs Sweet and Stephens clad in mucky denim fatigues as they caroused with the local hoi polloi. Whether I liked it or not, the wheel of fortune had recently awarded me responsibility for the well-being of these two soldiers.

On being drafting into the Army some months earlier, in order to ease the traumas of military service, I had decided to seek a commission. When my temerity was eventually rewarded with the coveted shoulder insignia, my plans for a cushier existence were instantly torpedoed by my father.

Even in the 1950s, £5 per week was a totally inadequate salary to support an infantry officer in suitable style without income subsidy. Having refused to grant me an allowance, dear Papa unhelpfully suggested that my well-being would be better served if I moderated my lifestyle and reduced my alcohol intake. As this course was unthinkable, secondment to the Colonies where pay doubled against a lower cost of living was the only solution. Thus, there I was on three weeks' leave, prior to joining the British officer cadre of the Royal West African Frontier Force in Nigeria.

The two gentlemen in the other bar had been fellow squaddies of mine who were now serving as private soldiers in the regiment's East Grinstead-based 1st Battalion. They too had applied for officer status but had failed to clear all the hurdles in the steeplechase selection process. Sadly, both of them regarded their rejection as a treacherous stab in the back by the establishment. This especially applied to Stephens who was a frightful snob and considered kowtowing to persons of inferior social status to be totally unacceptable.

Their ill-conceived remedy was to meet military authority head on, which was to end in tears for both of them. They should have taken a leaf out of my book. I have always followed the philosophy that if you can't beat them, join them; and then pursue your own agenda on their territory.

My pal Joe Taylor, the sartorially elegant landlord's son, suddenly nudged me in the ribs. 'What on earth are you staring at in the tap room? You look as if you have seen a ghost.'

'I have. Two ghosts,' I replied. 'Hang on, Joe, I will be back in a moment.'

Carving my passage with difficulty through an anxious closing-time throng, I eventually managed to reach my comrades-in-arms.

'What the hell are you two up to and why are you covered in shit?'

'Hey, Jingles, how great to see you again. We are covered in shit because, as usual in this bloody army, we are in the shit. We got bored with boiler room jankers which, as I am sure you will remember, is a pain in the arse. Fortunately, your old sparring partner Nick Burk was on guard and gave us the long blink so we hopped over the wall and took a train into Brighton for a laugh.'

As Peter Stephens had used my recruit nickname, I returned the compliment.

'Well, Hockey, as the pub is closing in about five minutes, what are you reckless rebels proposing to do then? If you are caught absent without leave whilst undergoing punishment it's military prison which is added on to your service time. Not much of a laugh!'

Adrian Sweet now cut in. 'Stop talking like a f***ing officer and behaving like a creep, Jingles. You didn't want to join the mob any more than we did.'

'Very true,' I conceded. 'But I won't be a f***ing officer much longer if I am caught fraternising with you two so you had better join me upstairs.'

I had recently finished with my girlfriend Val because of her indiscretions with one Dave Lynch whilst I was up to my neck in muck and bullets in Aldershot. To be honest, this had been a payback for my bestowing a similar compliment on his fiancée a year earlier. Anyway, the romantic severance meant that I was now free to join Joe's card school in the upper reaches of his father's pub. Such gatherings were a regular Friday and Saturday night event where the favoured game was Three Card Brag.

On this occasion we needed two tables to accommodate everyone seeking financial embarrassment. On our pitch, apart from my Army renegades, Joe and I were joined by two more punters. The most dangerous of these was Paul Marco, a somewhat oily modelling agent from the salubrious Hove ghetto. Glinting from a sallow, aquiline visage his flinty blue eyes were as adept at card call dissembling as they were in luring a series of beauties to his bed.

The other chancer was the corpulent George Coker who, if it had not been for his charm and affability, would have been banned from playing. This was because, due to being overindulged by doting parents, his wealth enabled him to gamble far too ambitiously when holding a lousy hand. However, if one was sufficiently brave or drunk to call his bluff, the rewards could be spectacular. Tragically, George was shortly destined to park his Austin-Healey under a petrol tanker at 90 miles per hour at the infamous Bolney crossroads on the A23.

The other table contained a couple of the pub's regular barflies plus two ex-Brighton College schoolmates of mine, Pete (Babyface) Butterworth and Dick Parsons. Notwithstanding his fresh features, lanky Pete was tanned, tough and mean following a six-month whaling expedition in the South Atlantic as a lowly deckhand.

Dick's angelic, chiselled good looks masked a mind like a steel trap which was to make him very wealthy in spite of his dedicated pursuit of the fair sex.

The questionable player at Pete's table was Doc, a middle-aged lush who drank whisky out of a vase and loved to wrap himself in a sheet with leaves tucked behind his ears! However, this reject from the medical profession was generous to a fault and often threw extravagant parties for 'The Crowd' at his mansion in Preston Park.

These soirées were co-hosted by Doc's live in 'maid', Magda, a swarthy but handsome girl who was one of many refugees from the Red Army's rampage through Budapest in 1956. Her specific function in this unlikely partnership was open to speculation, but she managed admirably when her partner suffered one of his comatose lapses. Thus, everyone was relieved that this stoic lady was present to help Doc sort out his cards for as long as he could hold them.

So there we were, a motley bunch of merry men on a self-destruct course until, at around 2 a.m., the proceedings were interrupted when Doc fell off his perch. Then, whilst he was being hunkered down on a settee in the corner, Joe and Paul had one of their tomcat spats over who was going to console Magda. Joe won this round of their long-running rivalry by claiming title to property and bedding and departed to an inner sanctum with his lusty Hungarian prize. All present gave a jeering round of applause as the petulant loser kicked over a side table and departed, crunching through shattered glass-ware en route.

Dick then picked an argument with Pete and George over the sweepstake result for forecasting the time it had taken Doc to conk out. It appeared that ridiculously large amounts of money had been wagered.

I was secretly relieved by the general disruption of events as my losses had already eroded my uniform grant down to the price of a hat and a swagger stick. This was, however, to prove the least of my worries.

'Can we have a word, Jingles? I think that Hockey and I have a wee problem.'

As Adrian actually sounded serious for the first time that night, I steered him to one side.

'As you are supposed to be thirty miles away, you have had a problem ever since the trains to East Grinstead stopped running three hours ago. Why start panicking now?'

My friend slurped on his pint of Watney's and grabbed a whisky chaser from the makeshift bar.

'Well, like Cinderella, we have a sort of deadline. Nick reckoned that he and the other lads on stag duty could cover our arses until

about four. Sergeant Roper is the guard commander and he normally surfaces around then and does the rounds himself.

I blanched. 'Christ, if that bastard nails you, turning into a pumpkin will be in Catterick [the most dreaded military prison]. But what do you expect me to do about it? When Joe returns to the human race he can get you a local cab. He shouldn't be that long, in case Doc rejoins the land of the living.'

'No, Jingles, that won't work. Firstly, we have blown what little money we had. Secondly, we would not be permitted to sit in a half-decent cab, covered in coal dust as we are …'

Hockey Stephens, who had joined us, interrupted: 'And thirdly, you can't trust these gossiping taxi drivers; word of our excursion could so easily get back to the wrong ears.'

It was only too clear where all this was leading so I pre-empted their presumptuousness. 'I trust that you are not even considering asking me to put my brand new Queen's Commission in jeopardy by helping you to cover up your crass stupidity!'

'Exactly,' my friends replied in unison.

'Well f*** you too!'

33

Then, as I saw their crestfallen expressions, the benevolent effect that alcohol has on me, plus my love of a challenge, took over.

'Listen, you silly buggers, if, as and when I win back my losses, returning you to the bosom of your regiment will be my prime objective.'

'Hey, Jingles, that's not fair,' they again managed simultaneously.

'That's as fair as it gets. Just pray that I win swiftly,' I said, in full realisation that my caveat would give me an edge so far as their future calling was concerned!

During this discourse, George, having discreetly regurgitated half a bottle of port into an ice bucket, joined Doc on the couch in sweet slumber. When Dick applied lipstick from Magda's discarded handbag to their noses, our chubby casualties looked rather like Tweedledee and Tweedledum after the fight.

With maximum encouragement and assistance from the military fugitives, we all rallied round to clear up the mess and restock the bar so that cards could recommence. As we were now down to seven punters, we pushed the tables together and decided to liven things up by playing with two packs. In fact, this was to have the reverse effect as it promoted more pontificating with our addled brains struggling to come to terms with the new odds.

By the fifth hand, in spite of Stephens and Sweet stacking in my favour, my funds were just about to run out when I struck gold. 'Babyface' dealt me the three of hearts, diamonds and spades: a magical prial of threes which beats everything.

Strictly speaking, in a friendly game, gentlemen were supposed to stack this all-time winner. Nevertheless, I played it cool until I recouped my losses, plus a smidgen extra for pain and suffering. With drunken optimism predominating at the table, I soon clocked up £57 10s which, literally, won back my spurs but there were hoots, sneers and curses when I revealed my hand.

Privates Sweet and Stephens were even more delighted than me over my good fortune as they were obviously eager to get under way with the utmost dispatch.

'God, Jingles, it's twenty past three already, please can we get cracking. You gave your word,' pleaded Hockey, whilst Adrian downed a hurried pint for the road.

Led by Dick, who thought that I had somewhat overegged my pudding, a chorus of good-natured abuse followed our passage out of the room and down the stairs to the pub's rear exit.

As the noisy taunts were likely to wake up Doc, I was relieved to observe Joe guiltily scuttling back across the landing as we departed. Whilst he hastily tucked in his shirt, a bedraggled Magda tagged after him, bewailing the loss of her much-needed make-up.

I was certain that everyone's trespasses would be forgiven and forgotten by the time of my next visit, and focused my attention on a more immediate challenge.

Unbelievably – particularly when one considers today's stringent road safety laws – at this time driving tests were a formality and MOT inspections a thing of the future. However, the greatest hazard when venturing onto the Queen's highway was that drink driving was socially acceptable, almost to the point of being fashionable! Unless one was completely incapable, it was standard practice to drive home after a night on the tiles. If you did something sufficiently outrageous to warrant being arrested, the Police would assess your state of inebriation via basic physical tests. These could be as mundane as walking a few feet along a white line or touching your nose with your finger six times in quick succession. Failing such intrusive inquisitions could result in a sobering-up period in the cells with a warning, or a nominal court fine enforced by a magistrate with similar habits. To illustrate how relaxed things were in this respect, it was quite normal on a long black cab journey for the driver to join you for a few pub drinks en route.

By today's legal standards, my drive from Brighton to East Grinstead all those years ago would have broken every rule in the book. I was probably at least three times the present permissible alcohol to blood ratio for drivers. The car, a 1938 Hillman purchased for £20 off a cook's corporal, had 13 inches play in the steering, bald tyres and erratic brakes. Also the exhaust pipe, which had fallen off some weeks before whilst I was attending battle camp in Wales, had not been replaced. This meant that the engine sounded like a printing press in full production, which had not won me too many popularity awards around the Southern Counties.

Fortunately, this dilapidated machine was conveniently parked just behind the pub where my two impatient passengers hurriedly scrambled into the rear seat.

'Bloody hell, Jingles, you are still driving this heap of crap,' said Adrian. 'What happened to the front passenger seat?'

'It came off its mountings during a romantic interlude on Ditchling Beacon,' I truthfully replied.

The air was then rent asunder as I cranked the engine into life, drowning any further complaints with a cacophony of tortured steel.

Our journey was traffic free so we made good time as we blazed a trail of insomnia through peaceful villages such as Cooksbridge, Fletching and Wych Cross. When we eventually arrived in the scattered suburbs of East Grinstead, Hockey urgently thumped my shoulder and screamed into my ear.

'For Christ's sake, park now or we will wake up the whole bloody town. It is only a five-minute walk to the barracks from here.'

'I am delighted to drop you off as far from the barracks as possible,' I shouted back as I screeched to a halt under some trees and killed the engine.

In the sudden silence, Adrian's voice echoed eerily. 'I am afraid that the situation is not that simple, Jingles. The area of wall that we have to scale is topped by barbed wire which is impossible to avoid without help from below.'

Having ventured so far, I had no stomach for further argument. In for a penny, in for a pound.

'Come on then, boys. Let's get this business over with as swiftly and silently as possible.'

Hockey then led the way to the chosen point of access. Having had my face thoroughly buffeted by scrambling bums and boots, I eventually saw the last of my friends as they disappeared over the wall to the sound of muted cursing and rending cloth.

I could not believe that the re-entry exercise had gone off so smoothly, and I was right to be sceptical. As I turned to hurry back to the car and vacate the area with utmost dispatch, I received a bowel-churning shock as the beam of a torch heralded an extremely unwelcome arrival.

'So what the f*** do we think we are up to?'

I did not need the light from a nearby street lamp for identification as Sergeant Roper's dulcet tones were a legend on the parade ground.

'Advance one and be recognised.'

Initially frozen in indecision, I felt some relief at the sergeant's incorrect picket challenge for it meant that he was probably as rattled as I was.

As it was to be another 13 years before the IRA resumed their vicious terrorist campaign, the likelihood of a guard commander in the UK being armed was extremely remote. However, the wiry little dictator confronting me was wielding an axe handle in a most disconcerting manner.

A physical solution was the only option open to me, which had two factors in my favour. Firstly, with my back to the light and a trilby shading my face, recognition was unlikely; secondly, I was twice the sergeant's size. The latter was the most important factor as the rat-faced weasel was a regimental sprint champion, so he would need to be temporarily disabled. Using the initiative that I was now supposed to possess, I rushed the hapless NCO and grappled him into the gutter, knocking all the wind out of him. Then, grabbing his torch and bludgeon, I hurled them over the barracks wall to the crash and tinkle of shattering glass, and legged it for all I was worth.

Although there was no apparent pursuit, I deemed it wise to lie low for a while, but my tribulations were not over yet. On returning to my rusty chariot I discovered that, as a result of leaving the side lights on, the last reserves of the aged battery's juice had dissipated. A phone box call to my father in nearby Lindfield for assistance was rewarded with some very unpaternal advice conveying eager anticipation of my imminent African departure.

And so it came to pass that my elevation to the very lowest order of royal patronage had a less than auspicious beginning. In the past six hours I had aided and abetted two military criminals, assaulted a non-commissioned officer and damaged regimental property. My encores are covered in other martial reflections later in this book.

4

Initiative Confounded

The Military's obsession with flag-carrying very much reflects a continuing respect for the pageantry displayed by our forefathers when they were on the war path. The displaying of colourful emblems not only boosted morale, but also identified the teams in opposition, thus minimising the risk of an 'own goal'.

It was not until the late nineteenth century, when increased ballistic efficiency dictated more discreet military tactics, that carrying regimental colours into battle was discontinued. As these banners thereafter became purely ceremonial embellishments, I failed to realise the intense degree of reverence in which they continued to be held. I was to be rudely enlightened!

Few of the tribulations in the life of a junior Army officer relate to physical stature. However, although the advantages of being short are limited, one of them is that a diminutive subaltern will never be required to carry the regimental colours on parade. At the time of receiving my commission, I was 6 foot 2 inches tall and weighed 11 stone 12 pounds dripping wet. Thus, as I even resembled a furled flag, my selection for this dubious honour was inevitable.

The discomfort of carrying and precisely manipulating an adorned 6-foot wooden pole in temperatures of up to 43°C was considerable. Nonetheless, although performing this noble chore sometimes caused me to regret volunteering for service in the Royal West African Frontier Force, climate was not the only drawback. Slotting a flagstaff into a suspended metal cup by your nether regions as you stare straight ahead could prove tricky. However, holding your bent arm parallel to the ground whilst supporting the colours for interminable periods of time on parade often verged on torture.

'Musa … Musa, where the hell are you?'

Whilst croaking this enquiry as I struggled with consciousness, I could both taste and smell the lingering stale tang of the previous night's party. Although still in mess kit, I had managed to discard my mosquito boots and negotiate myself sufficiently under the bed's netting canopy to deny most of my body to thirsty winged invaders. The mud-walled thatched hut, which was my home, was already sultry from the new day's scorching sun. Buggins, my fox terrier cocktail hound, was barking, Plato the African Grey parrot was squawking, and I had the king and queen of all hangovers.

In addition to these woes, in exactly 40 minutes' time, at 9.30 a.m., I was due to be carrying the colours in a full ceremonial parade. This was in honour of Leo Mendassa, the Minister of Defence elect, one of many senior Nigerians itching for the advent of independence due at the end of the following year.

'Yes, massa.'

As usual, this servile form of address was the nearest Musa got to exhibiting any form of respect as he casually shuffled over to roll back my mosquito net. Although officially my 'boy', he was probably old enough to be my grandfather as he could remember Lord Lugard's army crossing the River Niger near his village, Lokoja, in 1906. The intrepid General was on his way to teach the Emir of Kano a lesson and add another pelt to the belt of the British Empire.

Physically small and skinny, Musa could only muster four toes on each foot and when, in moments of extreme happiness or sadness he cried like a baby, his ill-fitting false teeth fell out. Nevertheless, in spite of his being selectively deaf, an inveterate thief and a hopeless batman, I grew to become extremely fond of him.

'Where the hell have you been Musa? I am supposed to be ready for the *babom* Lagos man parade,' I wincingly shouted.

The object of my wrath shrugged. 'I call you seven thirty, you say me f**k off, I obey orders.'

I decided against further assertion of authority as I urgently needed maximum cooperation from a man who was quite likely to suddenly disappear if I got him into a strop.

'OK, but I need to get into my best uniform "one time" or we will both be out of work.'

As Musa sprang into what little life was left in him, I was glad to hear Sergeant Oturkbo's voice hailing me through a small side window. He was one of the two-man guard assigned to escort me as I conveyed the regimental colours from the nearby officers' mess to the parade ground almost a mile away. It was most reassuring to see the Hausa NCO's cheerful, intelligent face as I pulled back the curtain.

The time had come to exercise something not dispensed by either the Queen's Regulations or my elaborate royal scroll of appointment: initiative.

'Morning, Sergeant, is Sergeant Bobella also on hand, and are there any other officers about?'

The answer was reassuring. 'He is ready and the coast is totally clear as everyone is at the parade ground.'

'Marvellous. Well done.'

My addled brain was still striving to engage as I vigorously lathered my face from Musa's proffered shaving bowl.

'Look, I am obviously completely in the shit. The only way that we can make it on time is by using my car and parking near to the action. Whilst I dress, you grab the colours from the Mess Sergeant and bring them back here; then we could be OK.'

Whilst Oturkbo departed on his mission, I completed my toilette and crackled into my heavily starched uniform as Musa affixed a ridiculous green feather hackle to my slouched hat.

Plato then went into a spate of foul swearing in an Asian accent, derived from his former owner, and Buggins disappeared to go about his unlawful business. Although this wondrous mongrel was a great source of amusement to me, his love of chasing goats and eating chicks did not win him any popularity contests with the African community. Also his favourite trick was to clamp his teeth on the trailing robes of the local traders as they cycled past and bring them crashing down with all their goods around them.

As Musa gave a last flick of the duster to my bulled boots, Bobella, the other escorting Sergeant, put his head around the door. 'Everything is ready, sir.'

'Great. Sergeant, what are we waiting for?'

I grabbed my Sam Browne and sword from my indolent flunkey

41

and ran out into the painfully dazzling sun to where the car was parked. Although only a humble 1954 Morris Minor, it did sport a sunshine roof which was most useful for the task in hand. As Sergeant Bobella squeezed into the rear seat with two rifles and my trusty blade, Oturkbo climbed in beside me with the colours threaded through the open roof. I then pulled the starter button.

'Bloody hell, that's all we need,' I exclaimed, as the motor went into a decelerating coughing cycle, denoting a dying battery. Its demise was soon confirmed by fruitless manual cranking, so with vital time running out, my reawakened initiative swiftly developed a desperate plan B.

'Right, chaps, I can only think of one further option to save my arse, which you will love as it gets you out of today's ceremonial bullshit.

'Sergeant Bobella, get across to the officer's mess, ring the B Company office and get Corporal Chico to sort out a couple of sergeants who know their colour escort drill. Tell him to make sure that they meet me with fixed bayonets before the last bend in the road to the parade ground, by nine twenty-five hours.

'Sergeant Oturkbo, uncase the colours and fetch my Army bicycle from behind the house, then kindly assist me to get under way. After that, you can both have a day's leave with your wives and concubines.'

My solution was far from ideal as I would be cycling uphill on a gearless wreck of a machine whilst wearing a sword and supporting the extravagantly decorated banner. Anyway, with only nine minutes until kick-off, my steadfast sergeants, now in fits of laughter, managed to launch me on my precarious way.

My troubles were by no means over yet. As I sweatingly struggled to maintain sufficient velocity to avoid toppling over, Buggins exploded out of the undergrowth. Obviously thinking that my antics were some sort of game, he bounded along beside me doing his utmost to grab the flapping standard. Although he failed in his mission, I was soon praying that the increasingly audible fife and drum band would drown his cacophony of excited barking.

When I reached the brow of the hill there were no sergeants in sight, so I was obliged to keep going, and discovered them waiting

around their side of the last bend in the road. This meant that, as I approached my new escort with my lance held high like Don Quixote, I was in full view of everyone on and around the parade ground.

Fortunately Chico, my wily Igbo clerk, was on hand to spirit away the rusty hobby horse and subdue Buggins whilst my new cohorts fell in beside me.

'Colour Party, by the centre quick march.'

It was precisely 9.30 a.m., but the exhilarated relief that swept over me as we punctually joined the massed ranks to the squeaking percussion of the regimental musicians was to prove premature.

Having completed a seemingly flawless parade, I immediately marched the colours back to the mess. Then, having dismissed the escort, I returned home to discard my sweat-soaked uniform and take a shower.

Apart from Plato, who kept repeating, 'Bluddafukabugger, bludda-fukabugga,' the dwelling was empty as my housemate, Lieutenant Rick McDougal, was off on manoeuvres in the bush. Musa was not in evidence and the absence of Buggins's lead from its hook suggested that he might be on a retrieving expedition.

I had just finished slaking my raging thirst from our one filtered water tap when there was an urgent rapping on the front door.

'Kemble-Clarkson, are you there? Open up at once if you are!'

The Adjutant, Captain Butcher, did not sound relaxed, but then he rarely was.

In the parlance of military radio communication an adjutant's call sign is 'Seagull' which is considered apt as it suggests that he flaps like hell and shits on everyone. Whoever contrived this piece of corny wit must have had someone just like my unwelcome visitor in mind.

'What's the matter, David, is my roof on fire?' I enquired on eventually opening the door. 'Good parade, eh?'

Butcher hissed in his breath as his rat-like features turned from red to purple. 'Your arse is the only thing likely to be on fire. Good parade? It was a bloody awful parade as it was ruined by your besmirching of military sanctity. And it's "Captain Butcher" or "Sir" to you in future.'

I opened my mouth to protest but was cut short.

'Don't even think of trying to give me any of your slimy civilian excuses. Mendassa and his party are leaving to visit the Residency soon and you will report to the CO in his office at noon. Is that clear?'

Without waiting for an answer, the Captain turned on his heel and swaggered off, most probably to seek out a new object for his venom.

My forthcoming appointment was not to be a social occasion!

Colonel Hill regarded me with distaste as I stamped to attention in front of the large oak desk behind which his obese form was slumped. In spite of gusts from an antiquated overhead fan, he was perspiring profusely.

'So, Kemble-Clarkson, what do you have to say for yourself regarding your disgraceful arrival on the parade ground this morning?'

'With great respect, sir, I do not understand what all the fuss is about. After all, it is only a flag.'

The moist bloodhound eyes regarded me with sadness as if I had just reported a family bereavement.

'A flag, indeed. What you have just done is tantamount to transporting a war memorial on the back of a shit cart. I will ask you once more, do you, by any chance, have any form of explanation for your outrageous conduct?'

I realised that the excreta in which I had become immersed was getting deeper by the second. 'Some administrative complications early today made it necessary for me to explore every avenue in order to fulfil my duty, sir.'

Was it my imagination or did I detect the shadow of a smile flicker across the colonel's grim, fleshy features?

'Could your administrative complications have had anything to do with your lascivious behaviour with the Quartermaster's daughter at the open party in the mess last night, I wonder?'

I decided that the discretion of silence was the better part of valour at this juncture of a one-sided conversation, so the CO carried on.

'Amazingly enough, I have reason to believe that you are not a half bad soldier.'

Slightly relaxing at this back-handed compliment, I almost jumped out of my skin when Hill suddenly turned up the decibels.

'However, you are quite the most undisciplined officer with whom I have ever had the misfortune to serve. That is why I am awarding you with three consecutive weekend orderly officer duties, starting this Saturday. Now, get out of my sight.'

Indignantly seething over the injustice of it all, I dismissed myself smartly, assiduously ignoring the gloating smirk on the face of Captain Butcher who was in the outer office.

Ever philosophical, by the time that I was back in the sunlight, I was already musing upon how Molly, the Quartermaster's daughter, would ease the burden of my undeserved confinement.

Rick McDougal was a chauffeur's son who, thanks to the excellent grammar school system – sadly destined to be dismantled by the Labour party – and his talented tenacity, had come far. As such he regarded being awarded a Queen's Commission with considerably greater awe than I did. Nevertheless, his charm and adventurous spirit had ensured that a firm friendship developed between us since we had been obliged to share our primitive living quarters.

My friend was now regarding me quizzically over the frosted rim of his glass of Star beer as we relaxed with our Sunday morning drinks. Our watering hole was the Kaduna Club's Red Fez Lounge, aptly named after the symbolic headgear of African acquiescence.

'I am very dubious about your proposition, Nige. I know that you see this as a way around the rules to fart in the face of the establishment but it could be regarded an exploitation of military tradition.'

'Rubbish, Rick, I am simply suggesting that you and I pep up the pathetic level of the "anything goes" games played after the monthly Mess Night dinners. Admittedly, we did manage to suspend Butcher from the roof beams a while back, but most of the soakings and humiliations are at the expense of us conscripts. My proposition is that by applying our imagination and initiative, we achieve a really impressive stunt that involves everyone.'

Rick did not look convinced. 'Holy shit, Nige, will you never learn? Anyway, as you can't really pull this one off by yourself, I am probably with you, but I could change my mind by next Wednesday.'

Neither of us was inclined to further debate, as we were still replenishing the moisture and energy we had expended earlier on the rugby field. We had been playing for an Army scratch team against the Kaduna Police.

As the Nigerians were far too intelligent to play the noble game with the reckless abandon of their white brothers, we should have had a comfortable win. However, due to our team's partying on Saturday night, hung-over tardiness delayed kick-off from hot 8.30 a.m. to scorching 9.15 a.m. Even though match time was restricted to 25 minutes each way, our lacklustre 24 points to 21 victory was a poor effort against a fledgling African side.

Rick suddenly chuckled. 'My God, but old Sokoto was really pissed off over the game this morning. Gave the ref a right bollocking for not starting on time, regardless, then roared off in high dudgeon with his forty thieves in their fleet of limos.'

Rick was correct: the conduct of the match had not pleased Kaduna's most celebrated rugby supporter, Alhaji Sir Ahmadu Bello, Sardauna of Sokoto. Although a fervent nationalist and vital pawn in the balancing act between the Colonial power and the Nigerian

Native Authority, the Muslim leader's passion for the infidel game was legendary.

I could not resist musing upon an extraordinary event I had witnessed whilst taking part in the Northern Province seven-a-side tournament earlier that year. Having worked himself into frenzy over the close-run final, the Sardauna invited all the players back home for a drink. His humble abode, courtesy of the British taxpayer, was a minaretted emporium straight out of the *Arabian Nights*. During visits from Westerners, the procedure was that turbaned and pantalooned minions would serve nothing but half-pint tumblers of whisky to all present. Not surprisingly, with 50 boozy rugby players on the loose in a palace known to contain a harem housing 40 concubines, things soon got extremely out of hand. Having stemmed two of our attempts to storm the stairway leading to the female quarters, the smiling army of exotic wine waiters suddenly exchanged their silver salvers for scimitars and grimly escorted us back to our cars.

'Hey Nige, either share your obviously amusing thoughts or, at least, get me another beer.'

I swiftly broke off my remembrances. 'Rick, I am so sorry, how about switching into pink gins? A litre and a half of Star is about my ballast limit.'

Rick shrugged and gave me one of his cautionary glances. 'OK, but remember that, thanks to your being all over Mrs Fortescue like a rash at the rugby club party last night, we have a lunch date. Good job her husband wasn't around. What is the set-up there?'

I put on a wounded expression. 'I shall rise above your offensive suggestion that I would even consider invading the sanctity of marriage. I might also remind you that I was very much the "philanderee" for a change!'

We both chuckled as I paused to order drinks.

'The story is as old as the hills, Rebecca Fortescue is suffering from marital thrombosis; she is married to a clot. Hubby George, the manager of Banque de Rhone's local branch, is twenty years her senior and a really Blimpish ex-Indian Army colonel. He even wears a monocle! They fled the subcontinent's self-governance about five years ago and will probably continue colony-hopping until they face up to doing their own washing up.

'So far as lunch today is concerned, that was really a pretty vague arrangement made under the influence. I don't really know the Fortescues that well and I haven't a clue where they live.'

The solution to our dilemma was close at hand.

'Hi there, boys! Fancy running into you two. I came back to find my red silk scarf that I mislaid here last night. Has anybody seen it?'

A likely story, I thought to myself as Rebecca plonked herself down next to me. She was attired in tennis gear which showed off her muscular tanned limbs to best advantage. The Führer himself would have been proud of this blonde-haired, blue-eyed, ample-bodied siren!

I met her flirtatious gaze. 'If I had found your silken scarf, I wouldn't tell you, as it would be secreted under my pillow for eternity. How about a drink to ease the burden of your loss?'

Briefly feigning a decision crisis, she relented. 'Well, I just have time for a quick one before taking you both home to feed you along with, I am sad to confess, a rather boring collection of George's friends. A large Manhattan, please.'

It is appropriate to comment here that interesting cocktails were the only good thing to come out of the 1950s CIA invasion of our African Colonies. These stalwarts, who masqueraded as Peace Corps operatives, were on 'Commie' watch following the arrival of the Russians in Ghana.

Rebecca made short work of her drink as she lobbed numerous double entendres into a breezy, bantering conversation. Then, with no further ado, we were on our way to enjoy some chicken groundnut stew with all the trimmings chez Fortescue.

The typical West African dish that we were about to savour was a delicious alternative to the more traditional Sunday lunch curry. Complimented by some deceptively punchy fruit punch, the cuisine proved to be the saving grace of an otherwise unremarkable gathering. Whilst Rebecca maintained a low profile, George paid Rick and me scant attention apart from occasionally glowering at me myopically like some gaunt Cyclops. The handful of other guests was comprised of vapid females and self-opinionated male expats, none of whom would have been capable of cutting the mustard in the real world back home.

My only involvement with Rebecca during the buffet was when she beckoned me over to the radiogram and thrust a small '45' record into my hand for me to play.

'Not Lena Horne's "New Fangled Tango" again,' I pleaded, having overdosed on the number the night before.

Rebecca then showed me the sleeve which displayed a photograph of an adolescent Elvis lookalike glistening with Brylcreem.

'I can tell you, Nigel, if this gorgeous boy was here now, you wouldn't get a look-in.'

The strains of Cliff Richard's earliest number one hit, 'Living Doll', then gently filled the room.

If the speculation is to be believed, had Sir Cliff by some miracle been present that day, it is highly unlikely that he would have felt inclined to compete with my evil intent!

Mercifully, the dreary party started to disperse far earlier than was customary as, unbeknown to me, it had been organised to precede a golf match. This involved all the windbags, most of their wives and Colonel Fortescue but not Mrs Fortescue. Somebody up there liked me!

To my surprise, during the general exodus, George suddenly became civil, even cracking some pathetic military jokes as he offered Rick and me cognac and cigars before leaving Rebecca to entertain us. Whether or not he thought that three was a crowd, I will never know, but my urgent signals to Rick soon ensured a company of two.

Rebecca silently slipped her hand into mine and led me up the staircase of her lofty home to a suitable bower. Memories of that balmy Sunday afternoon and the learning curves that the experienced older woman can bestow still linger. However, as others played golf, I was sowing the seeds of a fairway which was to lead me into some very tricky bunkers!

'Time to commence our mission,' I muttered to Rick as, with the rest of the Zaria officer compliment, we spilled out of the amorphous thatched mess bungalow onto its parched lawn. It was the monthly officers' soirée so, having toasted our young Queen, murdered the port and choked on cigars, it was now time to forget rank and get silly.

As the assembled company emptied proffered drinks trays, flickering torchlight dazzlingly pinpointed the medals and insignia that adorned an array of colourful mess kits. One of the many quirky facets of *Homo sapiens* at play – so often demonstrated at hunt, Highland and fancy dress balls – is that the more elaborate the dress, the less dignified the behaviour.

'As I told you last Sunday morning, Nige, I am far from comfortable with your enterprise.'

'Our enterprise,' I corrected. 'So let's get cracking and no more drinks until we have revolutionised Army after-dinner culture.'

Dodging round the regimental bandsmen, who were forming up with their devices of acoustical torture, we discreetly departed through a gap in the bougainvillea hedge. Our first objective was a crossroads on the way to the parade ground where the instrument of our plot was located in the form of a Japanese anti-tank gun. The relic was a monument to West Africa's Chindit soldiers who had fought with great bravery against the Yellow Peril in Burma during the Second World War.

I had already ascertained that the weapon's two rubber-rimmed wheels rotated freely, so trundling it to the mess garden's perimeter hedge posed no problems. The stage was set but, in order to achieve our objective, some serious ingenuity and initiative had to come into play!

'OK, Nige, you load the barrel with grapefruit and I will pop back to the house and grab the thunderflashes.'

I was delighted to observe that Rick had now got thoroughly into the spirit of things as I used brute force and a tree branch to wedge three grapefruit down the gun barrel. My friend soon returned with several of the bomb simulator fireworks, normally used on training exercises.

'These things are going to be quite punchy in a confined space. What do you reckon, two?'

'Well, Rick, I have really jammed up the barrel and we mustn't have a misfire so let's use three. As the breech block is missing, we must find something to close the back end, though.'

At that moment the raucous conversations taking place nearby became more audible as the fifes and drums paused for a breather and we could clearly hear falsetto whine of the Adjutant's voice.

'Come on, chaps, time for a boat race. Where the hell are our "heavenly civvies", I haven't seen them since dinner.'

'Trust that little shit to spot our absence. We can't muck around any more, Rick. I've got it; as we are wearing mosquito boots, we can use our feet to seal the breech.'

So our artillery venture proceeded, with horrendously effective results! As the pre-triggered thunderflashes detonated there was a substantial explosion and simultaneous blinding flashes from both ends of the gun. Having been raked by the back blast, Rick and I apparently made a ghoulish impression as we staggered from the ensuing pall of black smoke, both covered in soot. As has often been witnessed in war, explosions move in mysterious ways. This was certainly borne out on this occasion as, although Rick was minus a boot and I one trouser leg, we were both totally unscathed!

A factor that we had foolishly overlooked when planning this escapade was the ground swell of civil unrest which was developing in the build-up to independence. Therefore, the main disruption

caused by our little prank was that the mess staff, fearing insurrection, instantly went to ground. The good news was that this included the band, whose departure was marked by a trail of fifes, drums and bugles interspersed with red fezzes and gold-braided jackets.

It was a tribute to camaraderie that the majority of our fellow officers regarded our irresponsible stunt as a huge joke. On advancing up the lawn, drinks were thrust into our hands whilst our backs were pummelled in congratulation. This adulation was to be abruptly cut short, however.

'Are you trying to turn "conduct unbecoming to an officer and a gentleman" into an art form, or what? My God, but you two are going to pay dearly for this outrage.'

I was delighted to observe that Captain Butcher was more spattered by muck and grapefruit pith than others present.

I confronted the weasel. 'Listen, David, you are hoist on your own petard this time. Mess nights: no rank, no rules; remember? It is all part of your precious code and you would look very daft if you made an exception over the use of some fruit and a couple of fireworks.'

Not to be deterred by the general mutterings of agreement, Butcher squared up to me. 'You seem to be conveniently overlooking your defilement of a military trophy. What is it with you, Kemble-Clarkson, do you have a personal vendetta against war memorials? I suppose that you will try to blow up the Cenotaph when you get back to London, which is going to be soon at this rate. McDougal, I am disappointed that you have allowed yourself to be led astray by this lunatic.'

Rick regarded the Adjutant with contempt. 'I make up my own mind, David and you are completely out of order.'

'Support this rebel, if you will; we shall have to wait and see what the Colonel makes of all this. He has gone home in disgust and left me to go and sort out any confusion you may have caused for the wretched soldiers on guard duty. I suggest that the pair of you hold yourselves in readiness for a cosy chat sometime tomorrow morning.'

As the little dictator stomped off to pacify the sentinels, the fugitives were cautiously reassembling. As a gentle chastisement for their cowardly conduct, their first task was to clean and buff up our plundered piece of Japanese ordnance, then return it to its site. This having been done, the party resumed with a vengeance.

Unfortunately for us we had, indeed, exceeded the limits of Colonel Hill's exasperation so, much to the Adjutant's delight, he nailed us on a technicality. In the little kangaroo court that ensued it was suggested that our escapade was tantamount to attempting a self-inflicted wounding which is certainly contrary to military law. For this we were both 'let off' with two orderly officer weekends apiece.

With Molly now back in Manchester and no duty visits to Kaduna scheduled, this was going to be a very long two and a half weeks!

Due in no small part to the cussed obstruction of her husband, my romantic interludes with Rebecca turned out to be more intermittent than either of us had intended. Indeed, the Bard would have referred to us as 'star-crossed lovers'.

George's strategy was simple but effective in that, whenever he learned that I was in the vicinity, his otherwise regular and organised life pattern would become totally unpredictable. The first instance of this was to plunge me into a situation which could have seriously jeopardised the cushy military niche that I was carving out for myself.

In the era of the cellphone it is now difficult to envisage the crude radio telephone systems operating in Africa 50 years ago. Making a connection to England could take 12 hours via the post office and, even with local calls, discreet telephonic communication was virtually impossible. Fortunately, at the time of our romantic initiation, Rebecca and I had devised a system to bypass such difficulties via pseudonym correspondence. My letters to her would be posted to Mrs Scarlet Pimpernel, care of the Kaduna Club; corny, but effective! It was via this medium, during my confinement for the artillery incident, that we planned our second tryst.

The plot was brilliantly simple. On my first free weekend, George was attending a Masonic event on the Saturday night. Whilst he was revelling secretly with this noble clan, he had ensured that Rebecca would be attending Lady Fiona Pilkington's 'at home'. As the hostess was one of her closest confidantes, with similar fidelity issues, my mail soon included an impressively embossed invitation to her soirée.

The stage was now set for an exciting reunion, apart from one vital detail: transport. My clapped-out Morris Minor was no longer sufficiently reliable to undertake the 40-mile journey to Kaduna on an intermittently tarred, corrugated dust road. Normally, I would have got my friendly transport officer, Captain Johnny Austin, to wangle me the use of a Land Rover. However, he was absent on three months' leave and Captain Butcher was responsible for the motor pool! Oddly enough, indirectly, Johnny did save the situation as in his absence he had lent me his fine Arab stallion, Beda.

Lieutenant Graham Foley was a reclusive, snobbish little prig who was no fan of mine, even though we did share a keen interest in horses. He was extremely piqued when I was chosen as Beda's custodian as his two mounts were sad nags by comparison.

We all treated Muslim leaders with due courtesy, but Foley's over-obsequiousness with Al Hajji Ramah had earned him the loan of a newish Desoto convertible. This chrome-toothed, metallic blue American megamobile, with its super-absorbent suspension, was ideal for my needs.

'Oh. Kemble-Clarkson. What do you want?' was the discouraging greeting when I knocked at Foley's door one evening.

'Hi Graham, playing polo at the weekend?' I asked with as much cheerful friendliness as I could muster.

Leaning against the door post to emphasise that I was not being invited in, he drawled, 'Local tournament over Saturday and Sunday. You really should learn to play instead of trying to break your neck by battling around the race track.'

'Unlike you, it is a sport that I shall not be able to afford when I get back to reality so I do not want to get hooked,' I responded pleasantly.

'As you are playing at home and won't really need it, could I possibly borrow the Desoto for the weekend? I just must be in Kaduna and my banger is not really up to the trip.'

'Certainly not. As usual, you are obviously up to no good and the Al Hajji will be devastated if one of his fleet gets so much as a scratch,' was the unhelpful reply.

I put on a look of sadness tinged with sympathy. 'What a pity, as I was planning to be away, I thought that you might like to embellish your game on a real horse.'

I was halfway down the path before I got a result.

'OK, you conniving bastard, you're on, Beda for the Desoto. If you prang the car, I will personally geld you.'

I was glowing with relief. 'You and whose army? Are you sure that you graduated from charm school with honours?'

So Saturday forenoon found me riding high on the wings of Eros as I rolled through billowing clouds of red dust en route to fulfil his mission.

I arrived at the Kaduna barracks in good time to sort myself out with accommodation and then attend the mess for some lunch with the officers on station. One of them was Rodney Fitzwalter, a delightful rakish cad with whom I had already enjoyed some wild outings. He was a cornet in the Dragoon Guards who had been seconded to the Colonies following a public brawl with a fellow officer over a lady's dishonour.

'Well, well; Nigel, my favourite militiaman is deigning to grace us with his presence. What mischief brings you to the metropolis this time, pray?'

Without giving me time to reply, he continued, 'Please don't go anywhere near the colours as I would just hate to see them flying from your vulgar transport. Where on earth did you acquire that Yankee spaceship?'

'The answers to your two questions are: the Pilkington bash and from an Al Hajji.'

Rodney managed to stifle looking impressed. 'My God, Nigel, we are moving in high circles. Regrettably, I shall not be joining you at Fiona's tonight as I moved in her daughter's lower circle! Do give young Angela my love, though, if she is in attendance.'

When I had been introduced to a few strange faces at table, an extremely relaxed repast ensued. In fact, by half past three I had become so relaxed that, in view of my taxing evening ahead, a siesta was very necessary. I was harangued mercilessly for exercising my sense of priorities and as everyone left to watch the racing at the Turf Club, Rodney popped his head back round the door.

'It really is a great pity that you are not competing on your satanic charger today. Although you are far too heavy to pull off a win, your whip duels with other jockeys when cornering are excellent entertainment value!'

Rested, recuperated and suitably black-tied, I parked the Desoto in Chameleon Lodge's forecourt at 7.15 p.m., having surrendered my invitation to a liveried gate boy. The magnificent three-storey building was in the red-tiled white-stuccoed Spanish style, set in a colourful 2-acre landscaped garden.

Along with his knighthood, the property was part of Sir Giles Pilkington's gratuity package for investing half his self-made socialist father's fortune in the Tory Party. As he was even more pretentious than his appointment, I was delighted to learn that Her Majesty's Independence Plenipotentiary to the Northern Nigerian Province was in Lagos.

On arrival, I was given a glass of champagne by a flunkey who was dressed in obligatory crisp whites with red fez and cummerbund. He then ushered me through to a comfortably furnished reception area, already buzzing with party atmosphere, where I was soon greeted by Lady Pilkington. Although in early middle age, the finely boned hostess cut a handsome figure in navy velvet, strategically embellished with pearls and diamonds. Regarding me with the conspiratorially mischievous expression of a woman who is aiding and abetting cuckoldry, she offered me her hand to kiss.

'Nigel, how absolutely wonderful to see you again,' she gushed. 'Do come and meet everyone.'

Rebecca, resplendent in a diaphanous red cocktail dress with gold accessories to match her hair, was on hand.

'I believe that you already know Mrs Fortescue.'

My lady was ready on cue. 'The Rugby Club dance, wasn't it? How is my stalwart warrior these days?'

'Firm and steady, Mrs Fortescue. How's the Colonel?'

'He has been dragged off to some dreary Masonic dinner, poor fellow; quelle bore. And it's Rebecca, remember?'

As we drifted into the melee, Rebecca's blue eyes regarded me casually, as if the weather was our main concern, whilst she whispered. 'Everything is organised. We have the guest house in the compound for as long as we need, and I have the key. We can slip out of the party individually in about an hour.'

'What about George?' I mouthed.

The reply was slightly muted with impatience. 'Don't fret on that score. He will get home late, probably too drunk to worry about me. If he does get inquisitive, I shall insist that I went on to another party with Fiona. He is far too much of a snob to dream of querying any story involving her.'

We separated to circulate with the other guests until a discreet departure could be effected. I made the most of this inflicted period by doing some bore-baiting and yummy mummy flirting whilst keeping an eye on the leaden progress of an Ormolu clock.

'The best-laid plans of mice and men!' At precisely 8.15 my world collapsed around me. Standing at the door, with obviously not the first drink of the evening in his hand, was George.

Rebecca, the blood drained from her face, was quick to respond as she rushed forward and pecked his cheek. 'Darling, what a wonderful surprise.'

But her husband was paying her scant attention as he leered at me malevolently and, with the animal instinct for trouble we all still retain, the assembled gathering fell silent.

'Lieutenant Kemble-Clarkson, no less. You are batting somewhat out of your league, it would appear.'

Sad to relate, with ingestion of champagne exacerbating my gut wrenching disappointment, the insult pushed me over the edge.

'In that case, maybe I should hit your balls for six, you pathetic little bank clerk.'

Instantly realising that my remark was way over the top, I beat a hasty retreat before the instant groundswell of outraged disapproval could crystallise. During my ignominious departure, I managed an apologetic nod to a seething Fiona as I tried to ignore Rebecca's disdainful stare.

Scoring a deep scar in the immaculate gravel as I rammed the Desoto's column change lever into gear, I sped out of the lodge's gateway at a furious rate of knots. However, prompted by the road's treacherous shale surface, my sense of self-preservation soon quenched my raging recklessness. It was whilst I was bringing my excessive velocity under control that, on rounding a bend, I was confronted by a dreaded 'mammy wagon'.

These juggernauts were a bizarre example of African innovation and enterprise. Comprising of open timber tumbrels, mounted on heavy-duty lorry chassis, they careered around like semi-scheduled stage coaches providing cheap transport for the brave and the needy. With their jerry-built superstructures invariably grossly overladen, these relentless conveyances had a less than impressive safety record.

Leaving no room for me to get past, the Grim Reaper's envoy hurtled towards me, its klaxon's bovine blare competing with the screaming of impotent brakes. It was then that the Angel of Mercy dealt me a card. Suddenly an open gate became available on my left so, not a moment too soon, I pulled the steering wheel hard over and shot through it into an orchard. Although, with the dexterity of a slalom champion, I managed to circumvent the trees, the forces of momentum were still inexorably propelling me towards a stone wall. As I braced myself for the final impact, the nightmare ended as the Desoto nose-dived to a soft landing in a large garden refuse trench.

Apart from some thoracic discomfort via being thrown against the steering column, my ordeal had left me remarkably unscathed. More importantly, so far as I could tell in the rapidly falling tropical dusk, the car had sustained no obvious damage either.

'Are you OK, sir?' A breathless Sikh, in a smart blue uniform and neatly tied matching turban, came rushing out of the trees.

'I am Ali the gate guard and I thought you would be kaput when you roared past my office like an express train.'

'So sorry to startle you. Bloody mammy wagon forced me off the road. I appear to be fine, thank you very much, but where am I exactly?'

'You are in the compound of Ghandi House Luxury Apartments,' Ali replied, beaming with pride.

Through the foliage I could just make out some pink domed concrete buildings in the failing light which were most probably homes to members of Kaduna's wealthier Asian community. This layer of Colonial Africa's ethnic strata dominated domestic trade and, as such, had become a vital part of the financial infrastructure. This reality became manifest when, in later years, Idi Amin and other independent African leaders severely damaged their nations' economies by expelling everyone of Asian origin.

'Well, Ali, I am Lt Kemble-Clarkson of the Queen's Own Nigeria Regiment and it seems that my car will have to remain here until tomorrow when I can organise military assistance.

Having given me an awkward salute, the sentinel produced a flashlight from his pocket and climbed down to examine the Desoto more closely.

'I do not think your most beautiful automobile is very kaput. I could try to pull her out with my American Jeep and make an inspection. I am also a mechanic.'

I shook my head. 'I appreciate your gesture, Ali, but, with the rear wheels three feet off the ground, it will take something more powerful than a Jeep to shift her. I shall tell you what we are going to do. You take care of my car until I return with an Army recovery vehicle tomorrow. Meanwhile, drive me in your Jeep to my original destination and I will give you twenty-five shillings [£1.25, an African private soldier's wage for one week].'

A delighted Ali immediately responded to an offer he could not refuse, and so within ten minutes I was entering the hallowed precincts of the Turf Club.

With my battered ego in need of recharging, I was delighted to find Rodney in the bar celebrating his afternoon's winnings with the Honourable Archibald Fanshaw. Like the Cornet, he was a raffish renegade and, following a Stock Exchange hiccup, his family were overjoyed when he joined the Nigerian Tobacco Corporation as a sales representative.

We were a perfect trio for a relaxed evening of revelry but I had left a question hanging out there which Rodney posed the moment I sat down.

'Well, what went wrong, Nigel? You are always the last to leave a party and it is only a quarter to nine now.'

There was no way that I was going to disclose my (soon to be not so secret) romance to these two inveterate gossips.

'I slipped off as soon as I could because the company was stifling. Most of those present were pals of Fiona's ghastly husband so it was a right festival of arseholes.'

Neither of my friends was convinced as they eyeballed me with amused suspicion and then Algey put his oar in.

'Hang on, Nigel, have you gone queer or something since I last saw you? There must have been loads of bored gals there, just ripe for the picking. What's happened to your old wanderlust?'

By pressing the point further, Rodney unwittingly opened up my way out of this uncomfortable topic.

'You are trying to tell us that you borrowed some flashy wheels and drove forty miles on a shit highway to spend an hour or so at a party. There just has to be a hidden agenda.'

I immediately fastened on to the reference to the Desoto and diverted the conversation by recounting my recent narrow escape. Both my friends found the story extremely funny; particularly my ultimate location.

'So, Nigel, you decided to crash-land your spaceship in the Hanging Gardens of Babylon,' Rodney mused. 'As Temporary Motor Transport Officer, I shall be on hand with a couple of Scammels tomorrow morning to extricate your garish missile.'

My uncharacteristic conduct was not mentioned again as we enjoyed a boozy supper. Sadly, by 11.30 we finally blew our diminishing acceptability by bursting into song and were, politely but firmly, persuaded to depart. Having managed to fall down the porch steps on the way out, Algie decided that enough was enough and weaved off in his sample-filled NTC Ford Zephyr. Rodney was keen to get back to barracks but, hoping against hope that Rebecca might have escaped, I persuaded him to drop me off at the Kaduna Club en route. I really had got it bad and my heart leapt when I spotted George's Citroen parked by reception on our arrival.

'OK, Nigel, I will see you by the Taj Mahal complex at 0930 hours tomorrow morning for the rocket retrieval operation. I trust that there are no sensitive lawns in the vicinity as my vehicles leave a positive signature. Night night, God bless and happy hunting.'

Strangely enough, as they were ideal for African rough driving, the revolutionary, hydraulically adjustable DS Citroens were still regarded with suspicion at this time. Thus, the Fortescues' green and white version of one of these bug-eyed monsters was a rarity. On passing by its sleek superstructure, I noticed that the keys were in the ignition.

As Muslim impromptu limb surgery had failed to deter thievery, initiative dictated that I take charge of the keys in the interests of security. Of course, my real motive was that, bearing in mind the upset that my earlier faux pas may have caused, I now had a perfect excuse to seek out the driver. Praying that this would be Rebecca alone, I entered the club in trepidation.

Having visited all three bars and the reading room, with the restaurant closed and deserted, it became clear that the Fortescues were not present. I retired to the Red Fez Lounge to consider my position and, as I sipped my second malt whisky, I saw matters with increasing clarity.

It was, after all, quite early for a Saturday night and, if I returned George's car to him, gratitude would surely override our differences. He would then invite me to stay when I would, at least, be under the same roof as my amour. Maybe George was a very heavy sleeper and it would be her that greeted me, or perhaps she would creep into my bed in the dead of night. In my state, the possibilities seemed endless.

On researching the Citroen's unfamiliar controls with limited success, I finally managed to kangaroo out of the car park. Then, stuck in preselected second gear, I miraculously found my way to the Fortescue abode. Having negotiated the steep driveway, I parked the car in front of the house and that is the last I knew until I was awoken by a persistent tapping on the windscreen.

It was bright daylight as my eyes painfully focused on the un-shaven, black wrinkled features of my tormentor who was peering at me through a side window. My mouth tasted like the bottom of a birdcage and my head throbbed like a hammered anvil as I struggled out of my mobile accommodation. On glancing at my watch I noted that it was 8.30 a.m. as I turned to the grizzled, gnome-like gardener.

'How nice of you to wake me,' I boomed with false affability. 'You have done a splendid job with the garden. Are the Fortescues in residence?'

The reply was pre-empted by a familiar voice from above. 'The Fortescues were asleep until you started shouting at the staff. What the hell are you playing at?'

The livid bony face with tousled hair and no monocle which glowered at me from an upstairs window resembled something from a Hammer Horror movie.

I tried the jocular approach. 'George, great to see you. I rescued your car and brought it back for you. It really is most unwise to leave your keys in the ignition like that.'

For one moment I thought that the poor fellow was going to jump down and attack me. Instead, he gave me some very bad tidings.

'My car is in the garage, you presumptuous blackguard. I have no idea who that one belongs to, but if you do not move it and yourself off my property now, I shall call the police.'

With that, he slammed the window shut and, having checked out the garaged clone vehicle, I effected a bouncing tactical withdrawal.

I was to learn later that, on attending breakfast that morning, George hurled his cornflakes at the chief house boy for laying me a place at table.

My immediate objective was to return to the scene of my involuntary crime and dump the evidence. As I started to get the hang of the car's Heath Robinson transmission system, little did I know that the disastrous start to the day was about to sink to a new low.

I was pausing at a T-junction by the rugby pitches above the Kaduna Club when a rotund, middle-aged blonde woman, bravely clad in red spotted shorts and a skimpy top, waved at me frantically from the roadside. Keeping a weather eye open for mammy wagons, I swung across the main road and pulled up beside her. God, but she was ugly!

'Can I be of assistance? You appear to be in distress. Do you need me to take you somewhere?' I sympathetically proposed, suddenly observing with alarm that the lady seemed to be verging on a heart attack.

'In distress? I am in distress because you are in my bloody Citroen, young man. How dare you offer me a lift in my own car. Get out, immediately!'

I was too shocked by this turn of events to speak as the harridan suddenly climbed into the front passenger seat.

'On second thoughts, you can drive me down to the club where we will phone my husband and you can explain your criminal prank.'

Fate is often governed by coincidental timing which was certainly the main factor responsible for my ridiculous predicament. From the woman's further ranting, I gathered that, thinking that she had lost her car keys the night before, she had walked home and was returning with her spare set to collect her vehicle when she ran into me.

'Please do you mind not yelling in my ear, I have a ghastly headache,' I pleaded.

'I am not surprised, you look like a waiter and you smell like a brewery. What do you do when you are not stealing cars?'

I decided that to conceal my identity in this situation was probably not wise, but I soon wished I had.

'I am an Army officer. Lieutenant Kemble-Clarkson at your service.'

I was instantly eyed with contempt. 'That explains everything. You are a Fascist. My husband is just going to love this scenario. He is on a special BBC mission with the Nigerian Broadcasting Corporation covering the country's liberation and the withdrawal of you Gestapo bully boys.'

That was all I needed to make my day. I was now at the mercy of some neo-Communist agitator. To make matters worse, it was people of this ilk who were putting innocent lives at risk by fanning the country's smouldering pockets of unrest in the lead up to independence.

We entered the clubhouse in strained silence and she ushered me into one of several telephone alcoves. Having bid me sit in the chair by the instrument, she leant across and called one Norman Livingstone, her breasts hanging over me pendulously.

'Norman, I think that you should talk with the man who just stole your Citroen, Lt Kemble-Clarkson of the Colonial SS.' She passed me the receiver. 'Explain your actions, if you can.'

The vulgar diatribe that then whined and droned from the earpiece does not bear repeating. I hardly got a word in whilst Mr Livingstone made two things crystal clear. Firstly, his opinion of the Royal West African Frontier Force and, secondly, his determination to pursue me through the courts till kingdom come.

Having resisted an evil temptation to ask her if a blow job was out of the question, to my great relief Mrs Livingstone stomped off without further ado. As soon as she was gone, I telephoned the barracks and managed to catch Rodney. He agreed to give me a lift to Ghandi Mansions if I told him what I had been up to all night. He did not believe my addled invention of events.

The salvage operation proved to be surprisingly tricky but, by 10.30, after a lot of shouting and cursing, the Desoto was fully operational again. I observed with considerable relief that, in spite of its ordeal, there were only a few minor scratches on the coachwork.

Not wishing to go anywhere near the barracks for fear of a police visit, I had had the presence of mind to get my bags put on one of the relief vehicles. Thus, having quenched Ali's tears over the state of the lawn with another 25 shillings and bade a thankful farewell to my saviours, I was soon speeding back to Zaria.

The first 'Pimpernel' dispatches crossed within a week. My 'How could I when I love you so much' theme matching Rebecca's 'How could you when I love you so much' indicated that the relationship was crying out for redemption. Much to Rick's consternation, the second letter that I received had me whooping around the *gidda* (house). I had already shared with him my intention to extend the 'golfing' afternoon fling into an affair and he had instantly expressed his views in no uncertain terms.

'You are playing with fire, Nige. I am not criticising you for bedding an attractive older married woman but you are overlooking the toffee-nosed military aspect. As Rebecca is wedded to a retired colonel, she would be regarded as another officer's wife. You must have heard about old Tucker when he was caught on the job with Captain Grimshaw's missus. He was instantly transferred to an outpost in the middle of the jungle and damned nearly died of malaria.'

Although Rick's warning had probably made sense, he was gagging to discover the latest news, so I put him out of his misery.

'George is off to some stag banking seminar in Port Harcourt the week after next. Meanwhile, Rebecca has arranged to stay with an old girlfriend of hers from India who just happens to live in Zaria. Apparently the old boy's radar is down at the moment as he is convinced that his wife will have no more to do with me on account of the Pilkington party debacle.'

My housemate chuckled and gently punched me in the chest. 'Just watch it, that's all, my crazy friend. Hey, there is another letter for you, but this one is from the local fuzz. What have you been up to now?'

I had not told anyone about the Kaduna incident with the Citroen and was trying to convince myself that the problem might have gone away in the night. Although I managed to force a fleeting smile as Rick passed me the buff envelope, my blood ran cold in anticipation of its contents.

'Wouldn't you like to know, Rick?'

On some bogus pretext, I rushed over to the mess and read the enclosed document in the deserted reading room. It was a notice to attend an appointment with one Inspector Basil Nelson at the Zaria Police Station in three days' time. The subject under discussion was to be certain allegations made by Mr Norman Livingstone in connection with the theft of his motor vehicle, etcetera, etcetera.

When I attended the meeting a couple of days later, in spite of his Western name, the inspector turned out to be a squat and remarkably ugly Nigerian. Although he spoke perfect, cultured English his manner was imperious to the point of hostility as he obliged me to make a statement covering my version of the alleged events. Having studied my responses, Nelson eyed me with disdain.

'A typical colonial situation. You are relying on the evidence of another imperialist to whitewash your criminal activities. I shall revert to you in due course but, meanwhile, you must advise me if you intend to leave the Zaria area. Good day, Lieutenant.'

As Rebecca was not due in town yet, I had to bear this cross alone. Nevertheless, I felt reasonably confident that, in spite of our antipathy, George would not hesitate to stand by a fellow officer and gentleman. I was wrong!'

The following week I received a phone call from Inspector Nelson in my B Company office. He sounded smug.

'Ah, Lt Kemble-Clarkson, I am calling to tell you that you are now officially confined to town limits as we are preparing to issue charges against you for larceny. Your friend Colonel Fortescue denies all knowledge of the incidents outlined in your statement. When I have finalised the formalities with my superiors, you will be receiving a visit.' He hung up.

Thank God someone else now decided to exercise some initiative, an event which was to save my (now very crispy) bacon! Ten bowel-churning minutes after my daunting conversation with the gloating Inspector, I received a far friendlier phone call.

'Morning, Nigel, how the hell are you? Still trying to reinvent military and equestrian tradition? Jack Preston here, it's time that we had a drink. Are you OK for seven thirty at the Railway tonight?'

I swallowed hard in optimistic confusion. 'Fine, sir, I look forward to it.'

Being the haven of ex-UK porters and ticket clippies, the Railway Club was virtually off limits to the Colonial upper crust, so was a secure venue. I did not know Chief Superintendent Preston, the local Police Commandant, that well, but he was affable company and had been a great sportsman in his day. He arrived at the Waterloo Bar bang on time, a few minutes after me, and came straight to the point.

'Sorry for the short notice but we have to move fast. Presumably my nasty nationalist zealot has contacted you already?'

'Well, sir, he phoned just before you did this morning and made me feel like Jean Valjean to his Javert.'

Preston gave me an ephemeral smile then fixed me with a stern gaze. 'No time for literary jests, I am afraid. I have to ask you a very personal question, to which I expect an honest reply devoid of chivalry. Are you and Rebecca Fortescue having an affair?'

I realised that this was no time for prevarication. 'We are, sir. I adore her.'

'And she is similarly fond of you, presumably?'

'I sincerely believe that she is, sir.'

'Then you are a very lucky man on two counts,' said the old policeman and went on to explain where he was coming from, concluding with a succinct summary.

'The bottom line is that, if this action goes to court, your lover may choose to corroborate your story. If that happens, Colonel Fortescue, who is a revered British figure, would be revealed as a cuckolded perjurer. This would mean that the little Commie shit, Livingstone, will have a far bigger field day than he would have done by just nailing you. Fortunately, the stupid bugger has just seriously upset Sokoto during a broadcast, which could help, as this case simply cannot be permitted to proceed.'

The relief that I felt was profound. 'Absolutely right, Superintendent. Thank you very much.'

'Lt Kemble-Clarkson, much as I am partial to lovable rogues, I am not doing this for you. However, if you are feeling grateful, I have just got time for another drink before going off to make some urgent phone calls.'

Within two weeks, the media were reporting the untimely resignation and return to the UK of NBC's political presenter, Norman Livingstone. Speculation suggested that his departure was not unrelated to an acrimonious confrontation with the Sardauna of Sokoto during a radio interview. The Muslim leader had become incensed when he was accused by Mr Livingstone of having been a British lackey and walked out halfway through the proceedings. At around the same time, I received an advise from the Zaria Constabulary that all pending charges against me had been dropped for lack of evidence.

In the ensuing months, apart from some civil disruption, mainly instigated by the militant Action Group party, my personal life stabilised. Liaisons with Rebecca continued to be too few and far between, but well worth waiting for and usually enriched by dramatic intrigue.

My enforced soldier's life was considerably eased when Captain Butcher was sent to Camberley Staff College on a course and Colonel Hill was replaced by Colonel Ralph Wallace. The new CO was younger and far more progressive than his predecessor and, as he had a wicked sense of humour, we got on well. Gradually, a succession of officers who were senior to me – which sadly included Rick – trickled home on completion of their tours of duty. It was when a bout of severe hepatitis obliged Major McKenzie, my immediate superior, to join the exodus that the unthinkable happened. Much to the chagrin of what was left of the 'old brigade' of regulars, Wallace put me in charge of B Company. The temporary appointment saw out my time in Nigeria and, on the Independence Day Parade, I had a command position so carried nothing heavier than a sword. Some other poor bugger had to hump the colours around!

It was at the officers' mess beano after the ceremony that I ran into my intense little police persecutor for the first time since my fraught grilling.

'Hi, Basil. Happy now that you have got your country back?' I chided.

His hunched little body quivered with indignation. 'Chief Inspector Nelson to you. Count yourself very fortunate to have been rescued from justice by your evil regime. Now that we are liberated from Britain's misrule, I look forward to a new, thriving Nigeria which will be free from corruption.'

As he turned on his heel and strode back into the babbling throng, I would have been horrified had I known then how tragically his aspirations were to fail!

5

Goodbye Sailor

As all seasoned mariners will avow, the relentless nature of the sea means that it must be treated with the utmost respect, and those who underestimate its capricious power do so at their peril. True to form, with my hubristic approach to the mortal coil, I only came to respect this via trial and error.

'I have located a firm called Bergen Mini Cruise that rents out small cabin cruisers, but they will need credentials to demonstrate that you are an experienced sailor. I know that you know bugger all about handling a boat, so how do we get around that?'

I was on the telephone to Egil Faeroy in Norway; a client and great personal friend whose pugnacious demeanour and physique belied an intelligent and generous nature.

'Come on, Egil; you are supposed to be a broker, so think of something. How about saying that I am a Royal Navy officer on leave?'

'Well, Nige, as the leasing manager is a neighbour and we often go fishing together, I may get away with it. However, I still think that sailing from Bergen to Kristiansand down our dodgy coastline with no qualifications is f***ing crazy.'

'Egil, you have forgotten that I am bringing Sandie along, who assures me that she is an experienced navigator. Otherwise I am sure that steering a boat cannot be any more difficult than driving a car on a windy day.'

I had to admit to myself that I might be erring on overoptimism as Sandie, my girlfriend at the time, was a zany journalist prone to gross exaggeration. I ruefully recalled that, while we were in Barbados a few months earlier, she had assured me that she was an accomplished equestrian. When I then hired two steeds for a canter along the beach, she grabbed hold of the first available palm tree and screamed

69

the place down. Could such bravado also apply to her boasted nautical skills?

As it turned out, this distinct possibility was never put to the test. Just before we were due to depart for Norway, my volatile blonde bombshell threw a tantrum over an imagined infidelity and absconded to stay with her mother in Nottingham. Or so she led me to believe. This made me even more determined to proceed personally with the planned excursion, regardless.

Egil was most unimpressed when I told him over the phone that my forthcoming voyage would now be a solo undertaking, and begged me to reconsider my plans. Although I stolidly refused to change my plans, I did offer a small compromise by agreeing to be subjected to some instruction in maritime skills prior to the excursion. My concession was reconfirmed on Friday evening when Egil and Brit, his dazzling elfin partner, met me at Bergen airport and checked me into the Norge Hotel.

On convening in the bar before dinner with more Norwegian pals, I was relieved when the chain-smoking, whisky-swilling Jan Peterson took a more laconic stance. With his arms around his long-suffering wife's shoulders for support, he shouted for attention.

'Listen up, everyone; stop giving our guest a hard time. Nige, as you are determined to drown yourself, we are flattered that you have chosen Norway to enact your dramatic demise. If you play your cards right we might even give you a Viking funeral. Anyway, to delay your martyrdom, we have taken the liberty of deferring collection of your boat until Monday to allow time for your education in maritime skills.'

It transpired that the next morning everyone present was due to meet up at the Solstrand Hotel in Os, a quaint fishing village on a craggy peninsula south of Bergen. It was here, close to his home, that Egil moored his triple-decked Moonraker gin palace. When we were assembled, the plan was to sail around the local islands where many members of the party had retreats discreetly known as 'huts'. During these activities, it was hoped that I would absorb sufficient marine know-how to give me a remote chance of completing my intended passage in one piece. Unfortunately these well-laid plans had not allowed for the typical pattern of a Norwegian weekend.

Norway has long been the ultimate socialist 'nanny state' which guarantees the general populus a wholesome living standard by imposing draconian taxes on bon viveurs. This particularly applies to alcohol, the sale of which is controlled by government outlets at four times the price of most European countries. Also, with zero-tolerance drink driving laws and limited late-night bus services, costly taxis are the only option for rural revellers to get home.

Taking these factors into account, it is not surprising that more hedonistic Norwegians wait until the weekend to satiate their needs. Thus, particularly as my presence justified a business expense charge, the likelihood of my hosts wasting free party time on turning me into a seaman was remote.

My welcoming dinner in one of the Norge's private dining rooms was a raucous affair reminiscent of certain scenes in the epic Kirk Douglas and Tony Curtis film, *The Vikings*. Traditional speeches, in which I loved to participate, were especially crass and by the time we were ready to move on, numerous uninvited females had joined the party.

Having infuriated the hotel doorman by stealing his hat, we staggered around the harbour to the Hawk Club which was Bergen's only late-night hot spot.

The venue was owned and operated by Oyvind Ellingson, the town's most bizarre local hero, whose entrepreneurial enthusiasm knew no bounds. Sadly, he was very much a victim of his own brash personality which combined the audacity of Robin Hood with the ineptitude of Don Quixote. His Hawk Club project was a typical example of this and imminent closure was only being deferred as not all the local policemen had seen the illegal naked cabaret. Sadly, this was not the establishment's only pending problem. As with his hamburger stall a year earlier, Oyvind's accounting policy, 'gross turnover equals net profit', was paving a very rapid route to insolvency.

Ellingson's increasingly outlandish enterprises would eventually lead to him spending time at King Olav's pleasure as a 'cereal' offender. This occurred when he shipped in a load of Kellogg's Cornflakes from the UK. Everything went fine until Customs officials discovered that the weight of the container did not match the cargo's description. Surprise, surprise: inside every family pack resided two bottles of Teachers whisky!

With a character of this ilk hosting a self-destructive Nordic hoard, it inevitably turned out to be a very long night. Even when the club officially closed at 2.30 a.m., only the faint-hearted were allowed to depart whilst the rest of us stayed on for a 'lock-in'. Then, as glasses were refilled and the ladies of the cabaret were encouraged to perform an encore, Oyvind wandered over and gave me a bear hug.

'Great to see you again, you old devil. I understand that you have at last decided to become a true Norseman. To prevent your ending up in Greenland, I have decided to join all of you over the weekend.'

The lothario's bloodshot, piercing blue eyes glinted at me artfully. 'Lars, my manager, can mind the shop whilst I and one of my artistes take his very fine Saga cruiser for a spin. You may recall my assistance in Voss when you started skiing in 1970, so I now insist on extending my tutorial by turning you into another Leiv Erikson.'

It was true that Oyvind had been most supportive when I had taken to the slopes for the first time a couple of years earlier.

'Oyvind, most learning curves would seem as flat as a pancake without your illuminating input. Just refrain from teaching me your trading skills that's all.'

By some miracle, our flotilla did somehow manage to assemble at the Solstrand Hotel's moorings late on Saturday morning. However, the hostelry's dining facilities proved irresistible and we did not embark until we had indulged in a revitalising brunch.

During the inter-island partying that then ensued for the rest of the weekend, I did not receive one piece of advice from any of the assembled maritime luminaries.

At an uncomfortably early hour on Monday morning Egil arrived at my Bergen hotel room for a 'too little too late' breakfast briefing. My old pal was looking as bad as I felt as he dumped an armful of large paper scrolls on the bed. He then unslung a tapered leather case from around his neck and pulled some odd-looking plastic rulers from his side pocket.

'Right, Nige; as you are still intent on this madness, listen now and listen good. If you can follow a chart and plot a compass bearing, you might just make it to my home in Os for tea, by which time I trust that you will have come to your senses.'

In spite of being somewhat piqued by this patronising remark, I helped Egil unroll and spread out one of the charts on a coffee table.

'OK, there's no need to be so bloody condescending. Of course I can read a map, I was in the Army, wasn't I? But what are all those target things dotted around?'

My friend raised his eyes to heaven. 'Those "target things", my friend, are navigation beacons and will probably prove to be your life's blood.'

He picked up a pencil and the hinged rulers which he edged into position across the chart and having inscribed a line wrote '190' beside it.

'Now this is how you take a bearing from the compass rose, and I have plotted the direction of your initial leg. The number should obviously correspond with the boat's compass reading but, if you check the beacons too, you will know that you are on course.'

Egil then went on to explain other navigational aspects and pitfalls whilst handing over several maps of Norway's south-west coast.

'I get the general picture but, if I am in effect beacon hopping, what do the little blighters look like and why are they shown with coloured circles around them?'

'Listen, Nige. The circles show the arc segments of beams to aid nocturnal sailing, which is out of the question for you, so forget them. Most of the beacons look like little white daleks but do not get too close to them if a red light is showing.'

I studied the coastal configurations more closely. 'I must say that they all seem to be a long way apart. Will I be able to find them OK?'

My friend withdrew a large pair of binoculars from the leather case and passed them to me. 'With those you can spot a flea on the moon. I am delighted to lend them to you but, as they are Zeiss and worth a fortune, please use the neck strap at all times, especially when you are on deck.'

So that was the sum of my naval schooling, and I was as ready as I was ever going to be. With a final reminder to keep to the right (starboard) of approaching shipping and give way to sail at all times, Egil left me to join my first command.

Looking every inch a sailor in a blue duffle coat and a peaked hat that sported a gold anchor badge, I bounded out of my taxi at the Bergen marina, full of resolution. My initial alacrity swiftly faded, though, when after half an hour of asking around the network of jetties, nobody had heard of Bergen Mini Cruise. It was only whilst explaining my predicament to an uninterested dockside cafe owner that all was suddenly resolved.

'You are looking for me. My name is Jarl and the office is by the car park. You must be Kemble-Clarkson, and you are late.'

These words had been grunted from an adjacent table by a hairy mountain of a man whose attributes obviously did not include either delicate phraseology or personal freshness. Wiping his unkempt beard with the back of a grimy paw, he shuffled over to the till. 'Tron, your coffee is still shit. This covers me and my client. Come with me, Englishman.'

Maintaining a smouldering silence, I shouldered my kitbag and followed the oaf's amorphous hulk as he pounded up the metal stairs to the parking lot. Having completed the ascent and regained his breath in rasping gasps, he lit up an untipped 'coffin nail' then led me behind a stack of leaky oil drums to his headquarters.

The rusting corrugated iron hut that boasted 'BERG.N MINI C..UISE' on a blistered wooden sign did little to inspire confidence. However, as I was bereft of other options, when, following a tedious fumbling of keys Jarl eventually opened the door, I entered its dingy interior and grounded my luggage.

'How the hell was I supposed to find this dump?' I enquired with uncharacteristic belligerence.

Deflecting a suspended paper fly morgue, the caretaker slumped into a scuffed leather chair behind a scarred wooden table and glowered as he pushed a typed form towards me.

'By using your eyes, city boy. If you want the boat, fill this in and show me your passport.'

Although it was painfully obvious that my host and I were not destined to become boon companions, the bureaucratic process was eased by two strokes of luck. Firstly, as I had not changed my passport job description from 'Government Official' since leaving the army, my naval officer masquerade was not challenged. Secondly, because my booking had been made by a substantial local insurance company, no deposit was required. The latter factor in particular was to prove a major blessing.

Having read my completed form, Jarl regarded me with marginally less contempt.

'OK, so you are not a city boy. But you would have to be a bloody officer, wouldn't you? Let's go and find *Sissel*, shall we?'

We returned to the marina and, as we wobbled along one of the floating pier extensions, I was most impressed by the gleaming array of handsome craft. Sadly, *Sissel* turned out to be the ugly duckling and I felt seriously disappointed on being ushered aboard her shabby fibreglass and timber 30-foot hull.

Breathing heavily, with yet another Teddy cigarette clenched between his lips, Jarl unzipped the front end of the boat's stained canvas roof. On peering into the cockpit, I was relieved to observe that the dashboard display contained no sophisticated gadgetry. In fact, all the controls were delightfully fundamental wheel, compass, throttle/gear lever and bilge pump, plus gauges to record speed, revs, electrics and oil pressure.

My immediate priority was to discard my now unwelcome stooge so that I could indulge in some trial and error unobserved.

'This all appears to be just fine, if you give me the keys, I am all set.'

The overseer regarded me truculently as he manoeuvred his bulk into the waist of the craft.

'Not so fast, Mr Kemble-Clarkson. I have to demonstrate some features of the boat and identify movable items. As you were so late and I need to start my taxi shift, this will be quick.'

Having been shown how to operate the greasy galley facilities and create four cramped berths via seat and bulkhead realignment, I was presented with an inventory. This covered basic accessories such as oilskins and blankets plus a small Norwegian flag and staff for slotting into the stern whilst at sea. Just before signing, I picked up a 5-foot baton from the deck.

'What is this? Another flagpole?'

My query inspired a patronising leer. 'As there is no gauge, you use that to measure the fuel level. By the way, I forgot to mention that rental costs include a full tank of diesel and a bottle of Calor gas for the stove.'

On signing the proffered form, I silently thanked my lucky stars for this information. I had assumed that the vessel ran on petrol!

'That's fine then, Jarl. Thanks for all your help. Why not get back to your proper job now?'

As my tormentor stomped flatulently back along the jetty, my patience finally deserted me and I shouted after him, 'That is the most intelligent remark you have made all morning! Are you really certain that you want to be a stand-up music hall comic?'

For a daunting moment I feared that I had pushed my luck too far, as Jarl stopped in his tracks and slowly turned towards me. Then, much to my surprise, he bellowed with laughter like some pantomime giant before resuming his withdrawal with a Parthian fart.

My sense of relief that the jibes had not caused grief swiftly gave way to a feeling of isolation as I realised that accomplishing the ambitious venture was now solely down to me.

My first destination on the 270-mile voyage to Kristiansand was Haugesund, some 75 miles due south. As *Sissel*'s cruising speed was 14 knots and it was already after 11.30 a.m., time was rapidly running out if I was to have a chance of arriving in daylight. Therefore, without bothering to unpack, I bolted an early lunch of gravadlax and goat's cheese sandwiches whilst plotting my course on the unfamiliar charts.

Before applying myself to the controls, however, I had a patriotic task to perform. In full knowledge of the antagonistic implications from reading naval novels, I rigged the Norwegian flag to fly beneath the Union Jack on the stern flagstaff. This saucy gesture was destined to backfire.

After the engine had spluttered into life, I made the first of a chapter of nautical errors by leaving my lines trailing from the jetty bollards on casting off. Then, having managed to escape from the mooring without striking any of the other tightly packed hulls, I realised that I had no idea how to get out of the marina. When I eventually found the exit, my elation was such that I almost rammed an American sailing vessel under power and was rewarded with a traditional Uncle Sam greeting.

'Hey, arsehole, are you blind or drunk? With the way you're steering no wonder you still have your buffers rigged. You are supposed to keep to starboard; that's to the right, you mother f***er.'

Ignoring this vulgar criticism, I immediately hove to and teetered around the boat securing the fenders that I had carelessly left hanging over the side.

So at last I was all set for my voyage down one of the most treacherous coastlines in Europe. Notwithstanding this, all I felt was a deep sense of elation on confronting the fretful azure sea as it creamed against a panorama of gull-streaked rock buttresses.

Unfortunately such lyrical musing allowed my attention to wander and I suddenly found myself closing in on an islet's gently sloping shore. Egil had emphasised that such configurations should be avoided at all costs as they indicate shoals. Alas, by putting the helm hard over to rectify the situation, I transgressed another golden rule by passing a channel marker on the danger side. Thank God, by the time a grating crunch made the hull shudder, I had already throttled back and accelerated in reverse which miraculously avoiding a grounding. On steering into more open water I silently prayed that no serious damage had been sustained and switched on the electric bilge pump.

I was certainly learning lessons the hard way and, to my consternation, when I next looked at the compass it read 97 degrees east. Although I soon brought the boat back on course, as I had no idea how far I had drifted, it was time for a beacon fix.

To identify a specific point through binoculars on land is often tricky, but for a landlubber riding choppy seas, it can prove well nigh impossible. It was only when I hove to that the sought-after image, which was barely discernable with the naked eye, suddenly filled my twin lenses. With its gleaming white surface, neat service ladder and blinking eye, the truncated lighthouse looked for all the world like a piece of Lego.

As the afternoon progressed, I began to get the hang of staying on course and identifying beacons whilst at full throttle. However, I became somewhat less relaxed when, on clearing the shore's island screen, the sea's choppy rhythm changed to a more powerful un-dulating surge. The good news was that, according to my chart, this stretch of ocean exposure was about halfway to Haugesund; thus I still had a good chance of beating the dusk.

So far, apart from the public hydrofoils that regularly passed by in the distance in a haze of spray, other shipping had been sparse. This situation was to change dramatically, but thanks to the diesel engine's infernal racket I had no warning of the event.

All of a sudden *Sissel* was assailed by a powerful wave which emanated from the bow of a much larger grey vessel displaying the lion emblem of the Royal Norwegian Navy. As it swept past at great speed, barely 10 yards away, I found myself staring into a host of jeering faces lining the bulwarks. The sailors' gesticulations made it clear that their aggressive manoeuvre was a protest against my mischievous ensign arrangement. Tubular deck equipment indicated that I was being assailed by a motor torpedo boat, and no fewer than five more followed in its wake. The effect was daunting and I was forced to cling desperately onto the wheel, convinced that at any moment my beleaguered craft would turn turtle.

After two more passes, my persecutors streamed off, leaving me with scattered accessories and an increased resolve to maintain my pennant configuration. But my tribulations were not over yet. As the turbulence abated, I gaped in disbelief as the anchor, which had been jerked from a foredeck mounting, fell overboard, followed by its entire unsecured chain. Although I regarded the equipment as superfluous, I felt much better after having yelled a string of foul curses concerning Jarl's indolence. Anyway, on finding myself back amongst the rocks and reefs again, I soon pushed my recent setbacks to the back of my mind.

A stinging downpour assailed me as I eventually nudged my way into Haugesund's small yacht harbour in the half-light. Having found some rope to replace the mooring lines that I had stupidly left in Bergen, I found a space amongst the press of other craft. Then, ignoring the fact that everyone else was moored bow on, I backed up car park fashion with my stern to the jetty. As I completed this exercise, there was a disconcerting splintering sound as the wheel twisted violently in my hands. Much to my chagrin I discovered, on inspection, what looked remarkably like part of the rudder floating behind the boat.

With the canvas roof now demonstrating porous qualities, I had had enough of being a sailor for one day. Having rescued my kitbag from a deck puddle, I made my way to the more salubrious surroundings of the colourfully gabled Saga Hotel which overlooked the marina.

The next morning I was cruelly awakened as bright sunlight lanced through my window, reminding my head that I had gone to bed having drunk far too much alcohol.

Forty minutes later, I was just starting to feel human again after some bacon, eggs and coffee in the room, when there was a spirited rapping at the door. I opened it to discover Nils, my seafaring boozing companion from the night before. I had sought his company on hearing from the loquacious hotel barmen that he was a local trawler skipper who might impart some much-needed maritime input.

With endearing Nordic lack of finesse, my visitor barged his squat bulk into the room and poured himself a coffee into my discarded cup. Sporting a grizzled soup strainer which failed to conceal his gapped yellow teeth, Nils was no Adonis, but his humourous twinkling blue eyes did much to compensate. Whilst scratching his bald head, he plonked himself on the bed and belched enthusiastically.

'Well, Nigel, that sure was a great session last night. You probably didn't listen to what I was telling you, but I still think that you are mad to attempt Kristiansand on your own this late in the summer. Anyway, what about your steering gear? Do you want me to take a look at it?'

I accepted my new-found friend's offer and, having downed 'hair of the dog' beers, we strolled out in the bright sunshine to *Sissel*'s mooring. Nils then stepped down onto the ledge of boulders which had caused the problem and retrieved the sheared rudder lath from the water whilst he inspected the stern area. When he had finished, I helped him back onto the quay and offered him one of my Gitane Filters.

'So, Captain, what's the verdict?'

'Well, Nigel, it could be worse. Your have only lost about half your rudder which will make steering heavier, particularly in rough weather but, if you follow the "shrimper" route, you should make

Stavanger. However, as you may have f***ed up the pintle, do not even think of going further south until you have had the damage checked out. I can recommend a good man for that.'

After sharing more beers and making a note to contact Dag Olsen Propulsion in Stavanger, I bid Nils adieu having promised to get in touch on my return journey. With that, after topping up my fuel at the harbour's filling station, I prepared for the 40-mile voyage to Stavanger. It was only when I was marking the bearings on the chart, that I realised I had forgotten to ask Nils about the 'shrimper route'. This omission was to create a dramatic addition to my growing tally of seafaring errors.

As its name suggests, the town I was leaving is situated on a *sund*, which is a sound or channel. As up until then I had only messed about in other people's boats, I was poorly versed in the rules of marine courtesy. Thus I was not sensitive to the effect of a vessel's bow waves when passing through a narrow waterway; particularly one which was only 25 yards wide in places.

As I got under way at full throttle, I was pleasantly surprised by the friendliness of the locals as they waved at me energetically from their boats. I initially assumed that this exuberance was inspired by their amusement at my flag display which had so displeased the Navy. It was only when I observed a particularly fervent admirer tumble into the water whilst painting his yacht that I realised the error of my ways. I immediately cut my speed to reduce the wash but, by this time, it was too late as the sound was broadening into a more familiar seascape.

According to the chart, I only had to travel half the distance of the previous day and this is where I got it completely wrong again. As it was windy and the sea was rough, I should have pursued Nils's far longer shrimper route to the east, which hugged the arc of the mainland and was protected by islands. Instead, I sailed as the crow flies across the Stavanger Bight, where I was exposed to one and a half hours of North Sea pummelling. The worst aspect of this un-necessary trial was grappling with the impaired steering as I skirted a reef in mid-passage whose jagged teeth seemed determined to devour me.

On eventually reaching calmer waters, I was just starting to relax

when I was overtaken by a coastguard launch which, for no apparent reason, turned back and circled me. With the guilt of my Haugesund trespasses still lurking, I felt rather like someone who attracts the attention of a police car whilst driving home from a party.

Having been scrutinised, an electronic loudhailer addressed me in Norwegian and then, when I maintained my speed and course, in English with Norwegian directness.

'Ship number R696, you will halt. We are coming alongside.'

I did as I was told and, within moments, the sleek dark blue craft throttled back beside me.

'What seems to be the trouble, Captain?' I enquired obsequiously as a tall, blond-haired 'master race' type attired in a snug naval uniform peered into my humble motorboat. After a lingering silence, he set his square jaw and regarded me condescendingly with his piercing blue eyes.

'In spite of the fact that you have the effrontery to flag superiority over my country, you appear to be sinking!'

I was beginning to feel like Peck, Quinn and Niven when they were apprehended by a Nazi cutter in *The Guns of Navarone* screen saga.

As my attention had been focused forward, particularly whilst grappling the ocean rollers, I had paid scant attention to matters inboard since leaving Haugesund. On now being prompted to do so, I was horrified to discover that a copious ingress of water, which was lapping at my heels, had canted the boat stern down at an alarming angle.

'Good Lord, Captain, you are absolutely correct. It must be due to my dousing as I crossed the bay just now.'

Having pulled our gunwales together with a boathook and told his crewman to stay put, the arrogant young officer stepped aboard. Without offering the courtesy of an introduction, he then closely examined my instrument panel.

'As I suspected; your ship is not in a seaworthy condition. Are you colour blind? That red light over your "bilge pump" switch means that it is not functioning; no wonder you are foundering. Also, you should not have been sailing this tub so far out to sea in these weather conditions. As you really do not appear to know what you are doing, I must ask you to show me your papers.'

My heart sank, as the only document that I had to hand was a copy of Jarl's rental agreement, which I immediately removed from my inside pocket and passed over. Much to my relief, the official's belligerent demeanour changed to one of reluctant deference as he studied the crabbed scrawl.

'Engelsk Marine Offiser, eh? Kystvakt Loytnant Per Arnonsen at your service, Herr Kemble-Clarkson. You are obviously accustomed to far larger vessels, sir.'

I casually acknowledged Per's snappy salute, half expecting him to click his heels at any moment!

'Totally correct, Lieutenant; but how do you suggest that I sort out the result of my defunct bilge pump?'

Before he could reply, his helmsman, who had been talking on the radio, shouted a message in Norwegian which was obviously of an urgent nature. My uninvited guest swiftly opened a locker under the dashboard and, having rummaged through buckets, bottles and rags, passed me a large plastic syringe with piping attached.

'I am very sorry but we have received an emergency call and must depart immediately. It will be tough work, but you should be able to siphon out the water in half an hour with this, after which, check the bilges regularly until you get the electric pump fixed. May I suggest that you fly the Union Jack only in future and, wherever you are bound, the best of luck, sir.'

'Kristiansand. Thanks and farewell, Lieutenant.'

As Per hurriedly piled back into his craft, the glance that he bestowed upon me before shooting off spoke volumes!

Having crawled at half throttle into calmer waters, I hove to and set about getting *Sissel* shipshape and Bristol fashion once more. I was not that surprised when the coastguard's estimated time for pumping out the hull proved hugely optimistic. It took me over an hour to clear the flooded scuppers and turn my attention to stowing kit and squaring away the ship's equipment. Then, having decided that my flag prank had run its course, I removed the Norwegian pendant from below the Union Jack before getting under way again.

As it was still only late afternoon when I arrived at my destination, I decided to defer seeking out Dag Arnonsen and do some exploring. Stavanger had changed dramatically from the quaint community that I had first visited in 1966, via an aerodrome terminal no larger than a farmer's barn. The rapidly developing transformation was solely due to the town having become the nucleus of North Sea oil exploration and production. This newly discovered energy bonanza was turning Norway into a super-rich nation of 'blue-eyed Arabs' (as the jealous Swedes had christened them).

In those days the oil and gas industry paid scant attention to environmental issues when developing new ventures. However, I was shocked when, on sailing around the new harbour facilities, I encountered a grotesque edifice which resembled a castle keep with portholes. Strangely enough, as the vast concrete cylinder loomed through the pollution, I experienced a weird feeling of déjà vu and it was not until I later established its identity that I realised why. What I had stumbled upon was a protective sleeve, shortly to be towed 180 miles out into the North Sea and submerged to protect the new Ecofisk oil production platform. I recognised the structure, as an insuring Lloyd's underwriter had shown me a copy of its blueprints a year or so earlier and asked for my input. Ironically, this revolutionary development, which was to pump billions of gallons of fossil fuel out of the sea bed, is now destined to become a marine ecological centre.

On completing my tour I found *Sissel* a slot in the old town's marina where I was befriended by the inevitable band of nomads who adore the discomforts of boating. My new pals took me to a dockside tavern where half-decent goulash was copiously washed down by beer and aquavit chasers. On eventually being requested to leave, we returned to my boat for a whisky *nachspiel* and I finally conked out on a half-made-up bunk at 3 a.m.

The next morning I was relieved to discover that the repair facility I sought was only a stone's throw away. Dag Olsen turned out to be a very jolly fellow who could easily have passed for Nils's twin brother. Leaving an assistant to take care of his workshop, he followed me to my mooring for a damage assessment which he cheekily effected from a vacant dinghy parked under my stern.

'Well, Mr Kemble-Clarkson, the bilge pump poses no problem and I can sort out your rudder in the time it takes me to locate a replacement, which should be sometime tomorrow. What concerns me is that the severe jolt to the stock and pintle could have strained the fragile integrity of the ancient fibreglass stern shell. I must, therefore, point out that there is a possible risk of your steering gear breaking away if put under extreme pressure.'

This was, indeed, an unwelcome message and the engineer chewed his grimy thumb nervously as he awaited my response.

'Well, Dag, overlooking the cost factor which would crucify me via my enormous insurance excess, I really cannot get involved with repairs that would further delay my trip to Kristiansand. Do you think that I am being reckless?'

'If you mean "without wreck", I believe that you will be OK if you know what you are about and proceed cautiously. Just remember that there is scant sheltered water en route.'

I decided to ignore his rather weak Norwegian pun!

'So be it, then, Herr Olsen. All I ask is that you sort out the rudder as soon as possible. I shall be staying at the Atlantic Hotel should you need to contact me; otherwise I look forward to seeing you tomorrow morning.'

The die was cast and I had already formulated a contingency plan to fill in the spare time. Having taken a taxi to my hotel and checked in, I went straight to my room and dialled a local number.

Anna Lisa Hoveland was the daughter of a Stavanger shipowner who had generated a fortune by having the foresight to replace his coaster fleet with oil rig support vessels. As her father was a client, our paths had crossed when she was an Exeter University student and I was nominated to organise her Lloyd's work experience course.

As she was a typical liberated Scandinavian woman, it was open to question who took advantage of whom, but we very soon became an item. Because I was seven years Anna Lisa's senior and deemed to be a wild character, neither her family nor my employers were too upset when our relationship proved short-lived. In spite of this, as she was easy on the eye and we shared fond memories, an intimate, if intermittent, ongoing friendship had endured.

However, as I had not made any contact since my last Norwegian trip four months earlier, I was relieved when Anna Lisa seemed thrilled to receive my call.

'Fantastic to hear from you, Nige. Let's make it an early dinner at your hotel. I have got just loads to tell you. Meet me in the bar at six; see you then, darling.'

I found her request for such an early meeting rather strange, but presumptuously put it down to overeagerness.

Commensurate with the progress of my marine enterprise so far, the evening turned out to be somewhat of a disaster, as my date had just become engaged to a German banker. Although I had to admit that the radiance of true love enhanced the lady's already striking good looks, I had soon had my fill of the wondrous Hubertus. Much to my relief, I was let off the hook while the night was still young when my hand was suddenly gripped intensely.

'Nigel, I shall always remember you with affection and hope that you are pleased that I have found my ideal man at last. I am leaving in a few minutes as Daddy is coming to pick me up. My wedding will be in Bremen next April with a massive reception at the Park Hotel, and I insist that you attend with whoever you are misleading at the time.'

They just cannot resist the final kick in the balls, can they, bless them? And, as it was a moment for gloating, I was not at all surprised that it was Mummy, not Daddy, who arrived to take Anna Lisa home. Mrs Hoveland and I had never managed to get the best out of each other. The harridan – who always reminded me of a cross between a galleon in full sail and a guards sergeant major – epitomised the age-old warning to bridegrooms: 'look at the mother'.

Following a mercifully brief encounter, mainly focused upon her son-in-law elect's wealth, on departure the Viking Amazon turned to me with a gloating smirk on her face.

'I am so glad that Anna Lisa has come to her senses at last as you are nothing more than a *meel shavenist peeg!*'

My reply was heartfelt. 'For people like you, I am perfecting it into an art form.'

In deciding whether to drown my sorrows or grab an early night, for once I opted for the wiser course. This was fortunate as, on collecting my room key from reception, I received a message from Dag that *Sissel* was ready to rock and roll.

Ominous dark clouds were scudding overhead as I steered my barque into the rain-pocked harbour's exit channel. Nevertheless, despite the weather, I was in high spirits following a good night's rest and a very reasonable bill from Dag for what appeared to be a neat job.

As it was only 9.30 a.m., my plan was to make the day's landfall at Egersund, some 60 miles south, which almost halved the remaining distance to Kristiansand.

I was just sorting out my fuel and water requirements at a nearby filling station, when a prophet of doom approached me. The 'sooth-sayer' was a tall middle-aged Texan in a red Houston Oilers football hat and matching anorak, whose sinuous body and bronzed features denoted a man of action.

'Hi pal, Bernie Foss at your service. How are you all doing on this dismal day?'

Because I have spent much of my life around Americans, unlike most Englishmen, I am not fazed by their spontaneous familiarity.

'Fine thanks, Bernie. My name is Nigel Kemble-Clarkson and I am bound for Egersund, en route to Kristiansand.'

'That is kind of adventurous, Nigel. Mind if look round your boat?'

As Bernie exuded an air of confident authority, I decided to indulge his curiosity.

'You are most welcome aboard my humble craft. What would you like to drink?'

'Just a Coke, if you have one, thanks. This is a real neat little deal, but where's your radio?'

'A luxury of which I have no need,' I replied.

'OK, so where is your crew?'

'Just little old me, I am afraid, Bernie.'

I received no resistance as I added a slug of scotch to my visitor's Coca-Cola.

'Did you hear the weather report this morning?'

'I can't say I did. No.'

'So, Nigel, you are embarking on a voyage in the North Sea on your own and with no radio, in a small single-screw cruiser, when minimum force seven winds are forecast. I tell you what, my friend, even after twenty-two years at sea, I would not sail with you today if you offered me a million dollars.'

When I failed to respond to this pessimism, as my intended course of action was now set in stone, the mariner chuckled good-naturedly.

' I am just not getting through to you, am I, young man?'

On my confirming that he certainly was not, we went on to talk of other matters and, by an extraordinary coincidence, it transpired that Bernie was a Hoveland Line skipper. In a way, this was unwelcome news, as it gave his warning greater credibility. Notwithstanding this, my pigheadedness won and we polished off what was left of the whisky with no further mention of my intended journey until he was departing.

'Real nice talking to you, Nigel, but you might have a better chance of having a nice day if you retracted your trim planes.'

As soon as he was gone, I studied the dog-eared manual which led me to an obscure switch that apparently lifted the hull's stern and depressed the bows for extra speed. Use in heavy weather, however, was not recommended so, with one more faux pas to add to my growing list, I adjusted the setting accordingly.

On clearing Stavanger's protective headland and turning south straight into a gusting headwind, I soon realised that the voyage ahead was to be no picnic. Then to cap it all, as my body was subjected to violent gyrations by the angry ocean, I sensed a nauseous tightening at the back of my throat. I had only been seasick once before in my life, which had been whilst crewing a 9-ton sailing ketch in a force eight gale during the 1964 UK Cross Channel Race. It had been a decidedly unpleasant experience as, in addition to violent vomiting, one's unbalanced equilibrium invokes near suicidal depression. Now, with a similar condition building up, coupled with being unable to leave the wheel for a pee, I was beginning to have second thoughts about the wisdom of my voyage.

Two hours later, with the weather conditions deteriorating even further, I had managed to regurgitate everything apart from my underpants. Fortunately my bodily emissions were being dispersed by the lashing seas and the bilge pump was coping. However, with my morale plummeting and Dag's forebodings seeming to shriek at me in the wind, I became convinced that the steering was beginning to fail. So, with the spectre looming of losing my rudder off a rocky lee shore, I made the decision to abandon foolhardiness in favour of self-preservation.

Sissel listed alarmingly as I turned her through 180 degrees but, once the wind and rolling waves were coming from astern, the little vessel's motion became decidedly steadier. Literally flying before the elements, I reached Stavanger in under two hours and immediately checked back into the Atlantic Hotel, having moored in their marina. My reason for using this berth was not simply one of convenience as, having now failed in my mission, it avoided confrontation with the waterfront sailing zealots.

I had intended to defer contacting my Bergen friends until I arrived in Kristiansand but, due to continuing foul weather being forecast, this was no longer an option. Therefore, following a hot bath and a revitalising late lunch, I decided that it was time to telephone Egil.

Although he found my account of events highly amusing, I did detect a note of relief in his voice after I told him that I had decided to abort the rest of the voyage.

'OK, Egil, I am getting together with our mutual friend, Harald Arnenson, for a drink tonight and popping in on Gundersund Lines early tomorrow morning. All things being equal, I should be ready to tootle up to Haugesund by lunchtime.'

'Christ, Nigel, does that mean that we might have to put up with your presence in Bergen again on Saturday?'

'As I have no intention of spending more than one night in a puritanical toy town, I shall definitely be there, so please book me into the Norge again.'

'So be it, Nigel. I will get the gang together for a welcome home party just in case by some miracle you manage to make it back in one piece.'

As we then concluded our call, I felt fairly confident that the lessons I had learnt the hard way should now ensure a smooth return passage. This would have been a reasonable assumption, had it not been for an unexpected shipmate!

Having set out just after noon the following day, my voyage turned out to be boringly uneventful. In view of the continued turbulent weather, I avoided the ocean inlet and followed the protected shrimper route. I then crept through the sound at an orderly 5 knots, praying that none of the locals recognised *Sissel*.

As I had taken the more roundabout way, it was after 4 p.m. when I reached Haugesund's quayside, where an enormous launch was in the process of docking. Whilst puzzling over its presence, I was pleasantly surprised to observe Jan Peterson cheerily waving at me from the deck. The mystery vessel turned out to be the Bergen hydrofoil, which I had not initially recognised as its foils were submerged. In spite of warning klaxon blasts, I steered to within hailing distance.

'Hey, Jan, what the hell are you doing here?'

'I have come to take you home before you drown yourself, you silly bugger,' was the boisterous reply.

'Well, I had better move out of this thing's way and get parked in the harbour. I will see you at the Saga reception area in about fifteen minutes.'

With that, I idled to the familiar mooring area, this time making sure that I tied up bow on with a stern buoy.

As there was a jazz festival happening over that weekend, Jan and I were lucky to secure the hotel's last available room, which we were obliged to share.

'Well, in spite of the fact that pulling a Haugesund bird is about as likely as finding a pig in a mosque, at least we have got separate beds, just in case,' my friend observed. His pessimistic prediction proved to be incorrect.

As so often is witnessed at German beer festivals and even Cornish Floral dances, civic soirées tend to dissipate the morals of young female attendees. This is particularly true of more parochial communities, and one would be hard-pressed to find anywhere more parochial than Haugesund. Therefore, when Jan and I ventured forth into a village square already buzzing with beer-swilling local youths, it was not long before we got chatting to Liv and Brit. Consequently, after much carousing, singing and dancing, our two new best friends allowed themselves to be smuggled back to the hotel room. Whether it was our mesmeric charm or the fact that Jan had brought some whisky to a spirit-free borough, was open to question; but who cared?

Sadly, as was his wont, my partner in crime had grossly over-imbibed and, whilst we were smooching to tinny radio music, he tumbled onto his bed and instantly passed out. With some difficulty in their inebriated state, the girls managed to tuck him in, after which I was left to entertain them on my own as best I could. In effect, it was a case of Jan being 'hors de combat' whilst I was 'combat de whores'! Anyway, I somehow managed to cope and it was only when an undetected menagerie nesting in my nether regions wrecked a later attempt at reconciliation with Sandie that I paid for my sins.

The curtain went up on Saturday's drama when the delectable duo slammed the door as they departed with a bottle of Scotch as an involuntary token of my generosity. On discovering this petty larceny when he later surfaced, Jan behaved as one bereaved.

'My God, Nigel, how could you let them get away with it? That means that we only have a bottle and a half left.'

'Come on, Jan, we will be back in Bergen this evening and, with the way I am feeling right now, I shall be dry for the voyage.'

My remark did little to appease his addictive anxiety. 'OK, but I shall need some beer on board as a back up.'

The signs of my friend's eventual enrolment in the noble ranks of Alcoholics Anonymous were becoming manifest, and a crate of Pils duly arrived on the boat prior to our departure.

Three hours into the voyage, after consuming ten beers, Jan was starting to get seriously tucked into the hard stuff and, true to form, becoming increasingly belligerent.

'Right, Nigel, we are heading into my home territory, so you can stop farting around with those maps for a start.'

'Hang on, Jan. Just remember that I am the captain around here and you are not in charge for once.'

Although this was meant as a jocular remark, I should have gauged my passenger's morose state of mind before making it. Following a highly charged silence which lasted 20 minutes and two lethal measures of whisky, I got a reaction.

'Kemble-Clarkson, you just don't get it, do you? I am the boss in my neck of the woods. I know every barnacle on every rock along this stretch of the coast and your steering is all over the place, which is probably because you are behaving like a prick and not drinking with me.'

It was true that my directional control was erratic as a result of the storm-tossed conditions and the fact that Jan was seriously beginning to get on my nerves. Thus, on the premise that allowing him to take over the tiller would inhibit his alcohol intake, I succumbed to his imperiousness.

'OK, you smart arse; the wheel is all yours. Maybe it is time for me to stop being a prick and have a Scotch before you drink the bloody lot.'

I had made yet another cock-up.

'Stand aside, Captain Kemble-Clarkson and make way for the master mariner who will definitely not need these.'

To my horror, as Jan lurched forward to take over, he grabbed the charts from the dash. Then, during my unsuccessful attempt to prevent him from jettisoning them, he bashed his head on the windshield and collapsed onto the deck at my feet. After struggling to regain control of the vessel for a couple of minutes, I had to face the fact that the only functional life form on board was me. I received but one piece of advice from my recumbent crew during a final moment of lucidity, which was as much use as a doorbell on a coffin.

'Follow the hydrofoils.'

With panic gnawing at my entrails, I blindly plunged on in a

91

northerly direction until some divine power miraculously guided me to the haven I so desperately sought.

When I then docked in my Bergen marina slot and the wheel went slack as the entire rudder unit broke loose, I knew that someone up there must still like me!

6

The French Plant

From time immemorial, humanity has striven to resist, repair and conceal the physical degeneration which is relentlessly imposed by the passing of time. In addition to the application of chemical compounds, an increasing number of women have, in recent years, taken advantage of surgical techniques to combat sags and wrinkles. Most men, however, although often keen to preserve their physiques via gym workouts and pounding the pavement, regard resorting to the scalpel as a narcissistic anathema. Much to the chagrin of my friends and colleagues, I was persuaded to transgress this code when still only in my early thirties.

The ever-present spectre, which rarely haunts the female of the species but can be the bane of a red-blooded male's life, is premature balding. Barring the recent fad for shaven skulls, a full head of hair has always been an important part of the stylish masculine image. I therefore became increasingly dismayed during my twenties on discovering that brushing and combing was becoming more of a harvesting exercise than a grooming procedure. Inevitably, romance was to bring this crisis to a head – in more ways than one.

'Honestly, Nigel. I can accept the fact that living with you is bound to be a moveable feast, but one real turn-off is finding a tonsured monk's pate on the pillow next to me each morning. At twenty-six years old, I really do not relish being escorted by a baldy.'

I naturally bridled at this cruel criticism. 'OK, fatty. Much as I enjoy your company, there is no way that my affection for you would persuade me to don a syrup.'

Fran realised that her remarks were well over the top. 'Darling, I would not dream of being part of your doing anything so tacky, but how come that a man who prides himself on being up to the mark is unaware of hair transplants? After all they are purely a relocation of what you possess already, by way of a little bit of skin grafting.'

I was now wide awake and becoming increasingly perturbed by the trend of the conversation.

'Well, that's as maybe, but I am not remotely interested. How come you are an authority on this grizzly procedure?'

Fran rolled out of bed and slipped a silk kimono over her ample curves.

'Well, Nigel, you can blame yourself. By killing off my career in advertising so that I can be at your beck and call, you left me with too much time on my hands. Whilst idly leafing through *Vogue* the other day I stumbled across a fascinating article about a new French clinic that specialises in surgical rethatching. The facility is called Sweeter Partings and they have a UK introductory facility in Wandsworth. As I had nothing better to do, I paid them a visit and you are now booked in for a feasibility evaluation at ten a.m. on Saturday.'

Readers may find this conduct unbelievably intrusive, but that was how this lady operated. Hurriedly donning a towelling robe, I followed my presumptuous girlfriend to our Parsons Green apartment's spacious kitchen.

'You can't be bloody serious. Wild horses would not drag me into a strange den to be prodded around by a bunch of quacks.'

Fran gave me one of her dangerous electric blue glares. 'Just hang on and listen before flying off the handle. The study that will be done is purely to assess whether the skin at the back of your head is part of your balding pattern. If not, it can be transferred to replace offending areas where healthy growth will then resume for the rest of your life. So what is all the fuss about?'

In order to avoid the risk of disrupting the rest of the weekend, I decided to refrain from pursuing the matter and effected a tactical withdrawal to the bathroom.

It was not until we were enjoying our regular Sunday lunch at La Meridiana with a group of pals that my pertinacious partner decided to raise the subject again. As details of my proposed mutilation unfolded, reaction from fellow diners ranged between horror from the ladies to disdain from the men. The most vociferous critic of

Fran's grand design was John Downing, a rugged press photographer who was one of her closest friends.

'What the hell are you trying to do, you crazy woman? Turn Nigel into a poof? If a man is short, ugly, bald or whatever, he has to live with it and not cheat by interfering with nature.'

True to form, realising that her prognosis had fallen on stony ground, Fran withdrew for a sulk at the bar in the vain hope that someone would comfort her. It was during her martyrdom that my strong antipathy towards the project was significantly diluted.

Sitting on my right was Blot, a particularly attractive brunette who, in spite of being unusually tall, pursued a successful career as a senior air hostess with BOAC. Although we had only met on a couple of occasions, her sensuality was riveting as she leaned towards me conspiratorially and fixed me with her emerald green eyes.

'Don't take any notice of all this boring crap from everyone; it would take more than a modicum of plastic surgery to impugn your manhood. For once, I totally agree with our mutual friend, you would look far better without your bald patch. We have just put a man on the moon and are living in a new scientific age, so why not make the most of it?'

As these whispered remarks were concluded, Fran reappeared and ominously grabbed hold of a jug of water.

'Hey, Blot, if you don't put my boyfriend down, you are in for a cold shower.'

My new confidante's laugh was just a little too effusive and shrill. 'OK, keep your tits on, I was trying to do you a favour. I think that Nigel would be crazy not to follow your advice.'

As the threatening receptacle was put back on the table, I stepped into the breach before the assembled company could chime in again.

'Could we please leave this topic alone now and discuss something really trivial, like Pasquali's sex life!'

The ever smooth and unruffled maître d', who was the object of my jibe, flashed his perfect set of gnashers as he shepherded the second course to the table.

'So you plan to have an extra long lunch today do you, Mr Kemble-Clarkson?'

Everyone laughed.

Much later on, whilst Fran and I were enjoying a nightcap back at the flat, having got rid of the last members of a card school, I decided to broach the contentious subject again.

'Well, you wretched girl, purely to satisfy my curiosity, I have decided to attend your Wandsworth probe. However, I would emphasise here and now that this does not constitute any form of commitment.'

As Fran's expression briefly betrayed a glint of victory, I was subjected to an impetuous hug. The consolation for my pusillanimity was that getting her own way was this lady's ultimate aphrodisiac!

The outward shabbiness of number 32, Telford Avenue, SW2 belied its elegant reception area, where I was signed in by a middle-aged woman in a crisp blue uniform.

Having briefly flicked through *Field* and observed the kaleidoscopic antics of some imprisoned marine creatures, I was soon ushered into a more clinical environment. Here I was greeted by two white-coated young men who purported to be trichologists and required me to sit in an orthopaedic chair with an adjustable neck rest. Next, whilst I was interrogated by 'Doctor' Falibois concerning my hair loss history, 'Doctor' Sacks surveyed my cranium with the aid of numerous combs and magnifying glasses.

After about 20 minutes my inquisitors withdrew to a rather pretentious antique roll-top desk for a whispered discussion. Then, with the air of someone about to present an award, the French 'specialist' sat down on a stool beside my chair.

'Monsieur Kemble-Clarkson, we are overjoyed to inform you that your follicular profile enables us to recommend you to Monsieur Partout for remedial surgery. I am only sorry to say that, due to his very tight schedule, it may be a month or more before he can receive you at his Paris clinic for your first procedure.'

By now I was totally nonplussed!

'Not so fast, gentlemen; I really have not got a clue what you are talking about. Who is this fellow Partout and what makes you think that I would dream of going to Paris for a "procedure" which I know nothing about and certainly have not consented to?'

It was now the medics' turn to be confused and Sacks swiftly stepped into the breach in resonant Welsh tones.

'Mr Kemble-Clarkson, we are so sorry to appear presumptuous. Nurse Gooding gave your wife some detailed explanatory literature concerning the treatment when she made this appointment last week. Have you not had a chance to study it?'

I shook my head. 'Study it? I have not even seen the material!'

Falibois took up the gauntlet. 'In that case we will give you another pack to peruse immediately; so sorry for the misunderstanding. Meanwhile, I am afraid that there is now a charge of sixty-five pounds due. However, this not only covers today's consultation, but it also represents a ten per cent deposit for the cost of your first operation.'

I was now flabbergasted, not least of all by the cost level being suggested, which represented thousands of pounds in today's money. Nevertheless, pride prevented me from making this the main point of my objection.

'Hey, hang on; how many operations am I supposed to be subjected to?'

Sacks smiled indulgently, as if he was allaying the protestations of a small child prior to a dental appointment.

'We have to remember that this is a surgical procedure, Mr Kemble-Clarkson. Thus, in order to minimise the possibility of post-operational discomfort, we estimate that you would need three sessions over the period of a year. To respond to your earlier question, Monsieur Partout is probably the world's leading cosmetic surgeon outside the USA, where he was trained in Los Angeles. Now back on his home turf, he can afford to confine his activities to Paris as competition is negligible in Europe and non-existent in the UK.'

Having by now heard more than enough, I decided to withdraw gracefully and consider my position. After bidding the two con-sultants a curt farewell, I approached Nurse Gooding's reception desk to collect the promised brochures. The lady smiled sympathetically as she handed them over together with a small white envelope.

'This is the information that you require plus your account so far, which you may prefer to pay now.'

I forced a humourless smile. 'I do not "prefer", if you do not mind; goodbye.'

I soon flagged down a black cab and within 20 minutes I was back at the apartment, where there was no sign of Fran. As I was geared for retribution, her absence was a bit of an anticlimax. However, this was probably for the best as, on consideration, I decided that I should at least read the Sweeter Partings material before sailing in with all guns blazing.

With the sun now well over the yardarm, I opted to review the situation over a beer at the Duke of Cumberland just down the road. As it was a balmy summer's day, I sat at one of the pub's outside tables and was into my second pint before my study of the glossy pages was completed. I then had to grudgingly admit to myself that the prognosis was most impressive, particularly as a painless procedure was guaranteed without the rigmarole of a general anaesthetic. What really got my attention, however, was a synopsis of 'before' and 'after' photographs depicting previous patients displaying their recreated manes.

By the time Fran sought me out, although I was fairly well hooked and landed, I had decided to get some Machiavellian mileage out of the situation. As my lover was in an obvious state of apprehension, now was the time to strike!

'Hi, darling, sorry I was out when you got back. I popped over to comfort Rosie as Robert has been up to his old tricks again. Stay put whilst I get a large gin and tonic and another bitter for you.'

By the time she returned with the drinks, I had refined my plot which I initiated by assuming a morose silence, thus firmly putting the onus on Fran to break the ice.

'Your old school friend really is a bit of a bastard. Rosemary has discovered that he has been fooling around with some married woman at his office for the past two months and she is totally … OK, stop glaring at me in that way. How did it go with Sweeter Partings this morning?'

I took a long pull at my beer before replying. 'It would have gone off a great deal more smoothly had you given me their brochure to read prior to the appointment.'

The lady regarded her knees contritely. 'I know, Nigel, but I was worried that you might be put off by the fees.'

Unbeknown to my partner, the bumper pay-out due to me from

98

the Goldfinger Posgate Lloyd's profit meant that expense posed no real problem at all.

'You are dead right there, my love, but before I consider your plans for rearranging my body, we must agree to a quid pro quo factor.'

Fran crossed her legs defensively. 'What are you talking about? I can hardly force a comb through my blonde locks.'

I chortled sarcastically. 'Don't try to play the smart arse with me; of course that lily needs no gilding. I am alluding to your steadily expanding avoirdupois. As the Parisian "chef de tête" cannot grace me with one of his miracles for at least another month, you have plenty of time to go on a crash diet. If, by the time my appointment is due, you have not lost at least a stone, all bets are off and I shall cancel.'

'That's so grossly unfair, Nigel; but I am sure that you will not be daft enough to pull out at the last minute as you will forfeit your deposit.'

'Wrong: my deposit has already been discounted against the cost of this morning's session, so I have nothing to lose except five hundred and eighty-five pounds; if you lose fourteen. What could possibly be fairer than that?'

Fran lit up one of my Gitanes and lapsed into silent contemplation as I popped in to take advantage of the pub's facilities. On my return she stubbed out her half-smoked cigarette and fixed me with a resolute stare.

'OK, you conniving bastard, you are on. Book your appointment with Marcel Partout and I will endeavour to diminish my Rubenesque shapeliness. As you are off on one of your jaunts to the Far East on Thursday, at least I shall be spared your nagging but don't blame me if, on your return, I am a bag of bones like Twiggy!'

I really was quite taken aback that my overindulgent girl had acquiesced to my wager so readily. Almost a month later my surprise turned to stark disbelief when, on my return from Bangkok and all stations east, I was met by a new, sylphlike Fran.

My incredulity was recharged when we joined, newly reconciled, Rosemary and Robert at the Hungry Horse in Fulham Road for dinner the same evening. Not only had Bob's erstwhile plump girlfriend similarly drastically slimmed down, but also it was apparent that neither lady seemed to have moderated their ingestion habits in any way.

'I think that these two are bloody amazing, don't you Bob? And it is great that they are having a well earned binge tonight to compensate for what must have been a virtual fast.

'Jolly nice of you to share Fran's self denial, Rosemary: what a pal.'

I was rewarded by a peck on the cheek. 'As my Robert will affirm; when the chips are down, we are the stronger sex. When will you ever learn that, Nigel?'

My dear old pal, who was a dead ringer for Dudley Moore and almost as funny without realising it, was obviously dying to offer further input. Nevertheless, he had the sense to wait until the smug duo were well out of earshot in the loo before so doing.

'Don't you believe their bullshit for one moment, Nigel. These girls have been squandering a small fortune on some new slimming drug. I can tell you, though, whatever the substance is, it has some pretty alarming side-effects. Whilst Rosie has been turning herself into a mannequin, her behaviour has become increasingly unstable and manic. She actually burst into my office a couple of week ago and threatened to maim my super-efficient PA in front of the entire staff.'

In view of Bob's obsessive, if transparent, secrecy concerning extra-curricular relationships with his staff, I opted to remain silent.

'Honestly, Nigel, had I not been the boss, I would have fired me. Anyway, Rosemary has now agreed to stop taking the medication, on the grounds that I discharge Adella. What the hell; it's better to be with a bloater than a bunny boiler!

'Careful, the devil's disciples are coming back. For Christ's sake don't tell Fran that I have blown the gaff, I really do not need any more aggro.'

As the ladies returned, Bob faked nonchalance as he lit up an extra-long Benson & Hedges Filter which looked more like a relay baton in his tiny hand. Had I had the sense to heed his forebodings, I would have been more circumspect and avoided a dangerous confrontation.

Prior to meeting Fran, I had struck up a relationship with a willowy redhead who was a legal advisor to one of my clients. Although

Daphne Deneuve was my senior by a few years and suffered from a squint and a lisp, she was passably attractive and always highly amusing company. Our transient fling had ended due to her being transferred to a New York operation, since when we had lost touch. I was, therefore pleasantly surprised when my ex giggled up to me in Lloyd's on my first day back to work following the Far Eastern trip.

'Nigel, my darling, how great to see you again.'

I was subjected to a smacking kiss and all-embracing hug which had a number of nearby brokers and underwriters guffawing.

'Daphne; what a wonderful surprise, I thought that you had been lured into the bosom of Uncle Sam permanently. Now what's with the broker's slip case?'

'I soon discovered that the American dream is not all that it's cracked up to be, so I have moved back. I am sure that it will offend your chauvinism, but I am now working for Willis Faber as a liberated lady broker.'

The erstwhile male-dominated Lloyd's market was still adjusting to the advent of women traders which had only been sanctioned a few years earlier. Anyway, I really was pleased to see the bubbling Daphne again.

'Well, bully for you, but I insist on taking you out to celebrate your return: can you make lunch tomorrow?'

'Sorry Nigel, I am booked. How about dinner at our old Savoy Grill haunt on Friday? You were always at your best at the end of the week.'

Being a self-indulgent idiot who invariably allowed adventure to prevail over common sense, I readily agreed. After all, what possible harm could there be in having a repast with an old friend? However, as mentioning this innocent tête-à-tête to Fran might have been tempting providence, I chose the more discreet path of mendacity.

'Hey, guess what? Fred Long phoned me from Seattle today. He is in town this Friday en route to Germany and insists on treating Ronald Pool and me to dinner. As you know, he is one of my main American producers so it is an offer that I cannot refuse.'

The ruse was well laid as Fred was impossible to track down due to his just having left his wife and Ronald was *persona non grata* after endeavouring to grope my lady at a dinner party. Nevertheless, in spite of my assured air of casual innocence, I was eyed with intense suspicion.

'Oh, what a pity; it would have been great to see Fred again, but I am bloody well not coming along if that fat little pervert of an underwriter is going to be present. I would really like to give your Yankee friend a ring though; where is he staying?'

As Fran had only met Fred briefly on one occasion, this gesture was totally unjustified. Nonetheless, it needed to be parried, which I achieved with imaginative guile!

'I haven't a clue. As he is due to be in Hamburg for lunch on Saturday, he will probably just doss down at the first available airport hotel. I do not even know whether he is landing at Gatwick or Heathrow so I am waiting to hear from him when he arrives.'

My blonde bombshell was now stitched up like a kipper with no way of checking up on what was planned for Friday evening. The pre-mobile phone era certainly had some palpable advantages!

'Well, you are looking dead shifty and I just don't like it,' was suddenly screamed at me in a most unstable fashion. Bob had not been exaggerating over the side-effects of the slimming pills.

My old flame turned up for our tryst on time and groomed to perfection. With her lustrous red hair tied back, subtly compliment-ing a russet two-piece mini-skirted costume which showed off her shapely legs to full advantage, she looked almost beautiful.

As we sipped dry martinis in the Savoy's American Bar, I was soon reminded of what excellent company Daphne could be when she was in a fun mood. Many of the anecdotes we shared related to our various experiences in New York where it became clear that my guest's recent venture had been a riot of hilarious faux pas. Our ebullient mood stayed with us when we adjourned to the Grill where more than a few eyebrows were raised as a result of our raucous behaviour.

In my experience, laughter is usually a potent aphrodisiac and, combined with scrumptious food and fine wine, a romantic con-clusion to the evening became increasingly likely. This became inevitable when Daphne was rummaging in her handbag in search of her lipstick following the crêpes Suzette.

'Hey, what's going on? That long green object in your bag looks remarkably like a Savoy room key tag.'

Long eyelashes fluttered as she screwed up her hazel eyes in a guilty squint. 'Oh, Nigel, I forgot to tell you. As I am presently staying with my sister in Hindhead until finding myself a suitable London flat, I rented a room in the hotel to avoid the bore of late-night travel.'

'Good God, my dear. You are either earning too much, or being madly extravagant.'

My hand was patted conspiratorially. 'Don't worry about a thing; I will swing it on my Willis Faber expense account.'

'In that case, Daphne, I insist on encroaching upon your hospitality so that we can enjoy coffee and liqueurs far from the madding crowd.'

The rest of this short saga is shamefully obvious and should never have happened. My rashest act, however, was settling the lady's room bill the following morning, as I was certain that her new employers would not agree to finance the cost of a river-view suite.

Resisting the temptation to have one for the road at the Duke of Wellington in Eaton Terrace, I dropped a tearful Daphne off at Waterloo. When there was no reply to my second phone box call to Fran, I abandoned the easier option for making excuses and directed the now impatient cabby to take me home.

It was 11 a.m. by the time I let myself into the flat, and I was instantly struck on the head by a hardback copy of *Exodus*, hurled at me from the drawing room door.

'So where the f*** have you been, you bastard? And don't you dare give me a load of bullshit about playing cards all night and accidentally falling asleep, like last time you disappeared.'

I swiftly decided to adhere to my golden rule in these circumstances, which is that attack is by far the soundest method of defence.

'How dare you interrogate and abuse me in this fashion when you live in a style way above that to which you were accustomed before you met me. Like it or not, I am sometimes obliged to exhaust myself with after-hours business entertainment which indirectly pays for your cushy life. Thanks for being so understanding!'

My instant counter-repost achieved the desired effect and Fran broke into a waterfall of apologetic tears.

'I am so sorry, Nigel, but I was getting really worried about you, particularly as you often have to bail Ronald out of trouble when he picks a fight with someone.

'Go and sort out coffee whilst I tidy up a bit before making us some brunch.'

Unfortunately, my overwhelming sense of relief blanked out my radar and I carelessly left my unlocked briefcase in the hall. As I went forth to achieve my mission, I was about to learn that the heat in the kitchen can become an inferno!

'So this is how you entertain the people who secure my lifestyle, is it?'

The challenge was delivered in a frighteningly menacing tone, but it was not until I turned from my kettle filling duties at the sink that the stark horror of the moment came home to me. In one hand Fran clutched the recently receipted Savoy bill whilst in the other she was wielding the unsheathed African dagger from the wall in the hallway.

To this day I have never been sure what occurred during the next 30 seconds, which I prefer to believe was an unfortunate accident exacerbated by the slimming amphetamines. I know that I advanced to meet the situation muttering, 'I can explain. Steady on now, I was a soldier,' or something equally crass. Anyway, the upshot was that I ended up skewered in the side by several inches of Hausa honed steel.

One thing I do remember clearly is that, as soon as the blood started flowing, Fran was far more horrified than me. However, when having ruined two bath towels and used up a kitchen roll, staunching was unsuccessful, stark reality had to be faced.

'Oh my God, Nigel; what have I done? We must get a doctor ... but he is bound to call the police and then I will be arrested!'

'My dear girl, as I am starting to feel somewhat light-headed, I think a quick trip to a hospital might not be a bad idea. Don't worry; I will just say that I have suffered a domestic accident.'

Oddly enough, during the ensuing erratic drive to the discreetly remote Saint Mary's Hospital Casualty department in Roehampton, my main sentiment was relief that my white Citroen sported red upholstery. A less than perfect morning was then not improved when, whilst I was behind a screen being patched up, I overheard the duty nurse on the telephone.

'Hullo. Sister West of Saint Mary's Hospital speaking; is this the Putney Police? ... Right. Well we have got a dodgy character here in A&E who reckons that he fell over whilst pruning his roses and impaled himself on a garden cultivator. As it is an obvious stab wound, I was wondering if there was any local knife crime last night. No? Well I have the guy's details should you need them, anyway.'

Needless to say, I was relieved to learn that my rapidly deteriorating weekend scenario was not destined to culminate in my being arrested! Also, as the wound had been inflicted by a very thin blade which, thanks to my expense account midriff had failed to reach any vital organs, I had suffered no serious injury. In fact, compared to the mutilation that I was to suffer at great expense in Paris, the Fulham episode had been a walk in the park!

Rue Manine turned out to be in the Invalides area of the sparkling French capital and it was here that I located the hostelry that Sweeter Partings had booked for me. Although L'Hotel Josephine exuded a somewhat seedy ambience, it was bang next door to the *clinique* where I was about to be transformed. This was particularly fortunate as my Air Chance 'red-eye' flight had taken off an hour late. Thus, on arrival, I only just had time to check into my musty, dustbin-view garret before reporting for treatment at 11.30 a.m.

On arrival I was greeted by a perky brunette called Denise, who, in spite of her petite form, sported enormous breasts which her olive uniform could barely contain. Having ascertained my details in her attractively fractured English, she summoned her employer via an antiquated intercom.

Monsieur Partout turned out to be a stocky chap in his mid-fifties, whose saturnine good looks reminded me of Herbert Lom when he played Napoleon in the 1950s film, *War and Peace*. Indeed, his richly decorated, wood-panelled reception area easily dated back to the period when the real diminutive dictator was rampaging through Europe.

My hand was clasped enthusiastically as I was addressed in Maurice Chevalier English.

105

'I am truly honoured that you have chosen to take advantage of my skills, Monsieur Kemble-Clarkson; you will not regret it. Please call me Marcel.'

I managed to extricate my well-pumped right arm as I matched the obsequious greeting.

'As your skills are legendary, I am certain that "regret" will not feature in our collaboration … Marcel. I am Nigel.'

The little specialist beamed at me smugly, revealing a row of jagged yellow teeth which, sadly for me, proved to be a harbinger of halitosis.

'I am afraid that Denise's English is far from fluent; however she is highly qualified and will be assisting me throughout your treatment. As the procedure takes some time, I suggest that we pass through to my theatre so that she can prepare you.'

The pert young lady's limpid brown eyes gazed up at me coquettishly. 'Do not have fear. I very gentle.'

The windowless room into which I was then ushered was a cross between a portrait gallery and a chamber where French patriots might once have suffered a German quiz! Whilst voluminously attired ancients glowered down from illuminated canvases, the dominant mural feature was a vast mirror with an elaborately gilded frame. Directly in front of this imposing artefact, a large brass throne, upholstered in black leather with adjustable features like a dentist's chair, had pride of place.

Having relieved me of my blazer in favour of a surgical gown, Denise seated me in front of a nearby sink unit equipped with some barbers' trappings. Marcel then addressed me as he laid out a strange selection of implements on a table under the mirror.

'Bon, Nigel. I am pleased to observe that you have grown your hair long in accordance with our brochure's recommendation. As you will have read, this will enable you to cover up any temporary scarring following the follicle reallocation process.'

Although this point was made sympathetically, I was starting to feel decidedly less relaxed as the reality of what I had let myself in for sunk in. As if to emphasise the situation, after securing surplus tresses behind my ears with slides, Denise snipped, lathered and shaved two specific cranial areas. Having laid waste to the thinning region over my forehead, she then carved a swathe through the luxuriant zone above the nape of my neck. Thus primed, I was handed over for sentence to be carried out!

With the dubious advantage of being able to monitor my ordeal via the large looking glass, I had to admit that Marcel Partout's dexterity was a wonder to behold. As soon as I was seated in the *grand fauteuil*, he grabbed a triggered plastic tube from a side table with which he fired a white powder into the two newly exposed patches on my scalp. The result of this weird popping barrage was an instant numbing sensation. He immediately followed this up by injecting the same regions in quick succession with a series of primed hypodermics.

To my amazement, the surgeon then plonked himself down on a stool next to me and offered me a Gaulois, as he lit one for himself. Although my preferred French brand was Gitanes Filtre, I gladly accepted the offer and inhaled deeply.

'So what's next, Doc; do I get a glass of champagne?'

'That is for afterwards, Nigel. Meanwhile, we must wait for a few minutes for the local anaesthetic that I have just administered to take full effect. While we enjoy our cigarettes, I shall explain exactly how the procedure will be carried out.'

Partout selected from his medical armoury a small tap-handled chrome tube which resembled an old-fashioned hollow key with no lock lever.

'With this simple device I am going to remove one hundred and thirty small sections of skin containing healthy hair from the back of your head. I shall then make the same number of circular incisions in the balding frontal area and transplant the grafts accordingly.'

I suffered a brief coughing attack as the shock of this gruesome prognosis caused me to breathe smoke up my nose.

'Good God, Marcel. This is more of a gardening exercise than a medical operation. How about planting some tulips and daffodils whilst you are at it?'

Partout regarded me icily as he slowly stubbed out his cigarette in an adjacent brass ashtray stand and addressed me in a controlled monotone.

'Monsieur Kemble-Clarkson, I have shortened the noses, enhanced the breasts, and even extended the penises of the rich and famous, so I take great exception to your impugning my skill and integrity. However, if you are afraid to proceed, please feel free to depart right now and I will even refund your meagre deposit.'

I immediately found myself in a crossfire between the surgeon's patronising mockery and Denise's contemptuous glances. As there was no way that I was going to be accused of cowardice by the French, my only option was to defuse the situation straight away.

'My dear fellow; I was only joking. You have obviously spent far too much time in the States and forgotten about the good old English sense of humour. Please continue with my treatment as soon as you are ready.'

Having fixed me with a noble stare and shaken my hand again, Marcel donned a white face mask, which sadly did little to absorb his odorous breath, and moved in for the kill.

Apart from some slightly disconcerting scraping sounds, it has to be said that the procedures to which I was subjected on that afternoon in Paris long ago, caused no real discomfort. I have to admit, though, that matters was greatly enhanced by Denise who, in order to constrain movement, buried my head in her cleavage for much of the duration. Notwithstanding this, my enhanced view of the operation via the large mirror did engender some queasy moments.

The first of these was to put me off potted shrimps for ever, as this was exactly what the harvested tissue plugs, which had been carelessly deposited in a dish beside me, resembled. My next grizzly ordeal was prompted by the bizarre French sense of humour. Having completed his frontal incisions, Marcel tipped my head forward to reveal a reflected image which looked as if I had been the victim of a shotgun accident.

'*Passoire, passoire,*' he chanted laughingly, which was immediately echoed by his nurse, '*Oui, oui; passoire.*'

I am the first to admit that my ability to converse fluently in the French tongue is sadly lacking, so I could only guess that my medical hosts were suggesting a visit to the lavatory.

'Marcel; are you seriously requesting me to visit the toilette in this bloody gruesome state?'

My tormentor gurgled with increased mirth. 'No, no, Nigel. I do not know the English word, but all we are saying is that you look like the bowl with holes that is used for straining water off vegetables.'

I am unlikely to ever forget the French for colander!

After what seemed like an eternity, the last implant was bedded in. However, matters were still far from over.

'Voilà. The surgery is satisfactorily completed. Nevertheless, it is now vital that all bleeding is totally staunched before we apply dressings. You may then return to your hotel for dinner and repose where excessive movement of or contact with your head must be avoided at all costs. I cannot emphasise this enough, Nigel, as any transplants which continue to bleed significantly are unlikely to be functional. And finally, no alcohol please, as this can interfere with the coagulation process.'

I had certainly got the message so, after an hour of mopping and dabbing, I very cautiously crept next door with my bandages making me look for the entire world like an inebriated maharaja.

I then spent a most uncomfortable sleepless night, obsessively sitting bolt upright in bed so as to avoid even pillow contact with

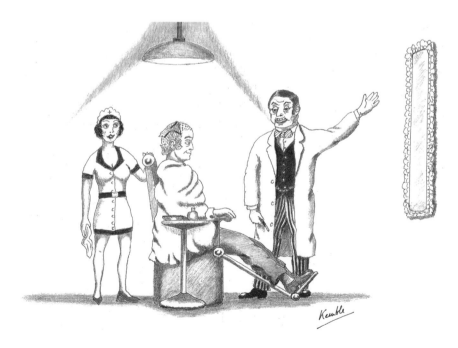

my copiously swathed head. Next morning following a hurried *café complet*, I reported for my 9 a.m. appointment at the clinic, where a bustling Partout surveyed his handy work.

'This is *parfait. Regardez, Denise c'est tres bien*. Nigel, I am delighted to report that, as there is no evident tissue disruption, you are en route to becoming a hairy hound once again.'

Although I did not feel particularly flattered by the specialist's simile, I decided to put up a bullish front.

'Well, Marcel, I should bloody well think so. Last night was the first time that I have ever been obliged to behave myself in Paris, and the experience was most unnatural.'

Denise gave me a knowing look as she flexed her ample bust. 'You are so *mauvais*, Monsieur Kemble-Clarkson. Maybe I will must put this right when you final inspect, *après trois semaines!*'

So there I was, all done and dusted. Light dressings were then applied, over which I gingerly donned a soft fedora and, having settled up with Partout in cash and kissed Denise, I was on my way to the airport.

One of the great foibles of human behaviour is the illogical tendency to allow incidental events to distort our sense of priorities. Due to turbulent cross-winds, my homeward-bound aircraft was blown onto the grass meridian beside the runway in the worst landing that I have ever experienced. My ridiculous immediate sentiment was, bastards: I have just paid the French a fortune for new hair and now bloody Air France is trying to burn it off again!

Although reactions to my pock-like scars from friends and work mates ranged between fascination, horror and derision, the process worked like a dream. However, via 'sod's law', my next half-serious girlfriend found balding men rather attractive, so it was a while before I considered completing the Sweeter Partings deal. By this time, as I was in the middle of setting up a business, my limited availability, coupled with grossly increased costs for the next phase, led to deferment.

I never have completed the transplant programme but, to this day, if I angle my face carefully, photographs depict me with an apparent full head of hair.

7

Secondhand Rose

I was now certain that I had never, ever met the striking young lady who was approaching me in the Savoy American Bar's only alcove. The rendezvous had been agreed upon two days earlier when she phoned me out of the blue and insisted that I had recently invited her to dinner whilst we were chatting at a party. An event of which I had no recollection!

Although this was obviously a set-up, the lady's piquant features and the undulating curves beneath her silk caftan immediately persuaded me to go along with the masquerade. As I stood up to greet her, she tossed her bobbed auburn locks and scrutinised me with a pair of lustrous blue eyes.

'Rose, how wonderful to see you again,' I dissembled. 'Do sit down and let me get you something to drink.'

Having let me kiss her on both cheeks, she fluttered a sadly fashionable set of false eyelashes at me.

'Hi Nigel: so the mountain came to Muhammad. You must have been more plastered than I realised when you insisted that we meet up again the other night.'

'Whatever. All's well that ends well, and here we are,' I smilingly averred as she crossed a perfect pair of silk-clad legs and accepted a Jack Daniels on the rocks.

As conversation flowed as freely as the drinks, I noticed that Rose's voice bore the faint rhythm of a brogue. Indeed, it transpired that her heritage was Irish Swiss; a formidable blend, as I was to discover.

The evening was a swinging success with a predictable pattern: dinner at San Frediano, dancing at Raffles and then back to my place in Tedworth Square for a nightcap.

Thereafter, as the lady was no one-night stand flibbertigibbet, we went on to share a roller-coaster relationship during the two months leading up to Christmas. However, this story is about how I joined the 'none as blind as those who will not see' brigade, when I was old and ugly enough to know better.

Rose lived in a Pimlico apartment which, like her, was fashionably and expensively furnished. The third bedroom served as an office from which, via a battery of telephones, she purported to run a modelling agency. As I was actively discouraged from visiting this room, I managed to contain my curiosity, in spite of the fact that it was staffed by a bevy of gorgeous telephonists.

The only downside of visiting Rose at home was having to put up with her fat, middle-aged business partner Norman, a 'defrocked' City accountant. This odious character seemed to lurk in every corner of her flat from dawn to dusk. In fact on our first encounter, I almost had a heart attack when he suddenly appeared at breakfast and questioned my presence in a piercing, plummy voice. Due to the belligerence of his challenge, I initially assumed that I had been caught red-handed by either a sugar daddy or an ageing husband. The state of shrouded hostility between Norman and I was not improved when it became apparent that his venture with Rose had a sinister hidden agenda.

In common with many of her female contemporaries during the heady days of the 'permissive society', Rose had a penchant for being as outrageous as possible. I certainly had no problem with this and it delighted most of my friends. However, she did make a suggestion one day that, in spite of the fact that I had been around the block a couple of times, almost shocked me.

'You would not mind if someone watched us screwing, would you, Darling?'

Not knowing whether or not she was joking, I trod cautiously. 'That would entirely depend on the circumstances and the identity of the audience.'

'That's great, Nigel, because I know an old Texan who can't raise a gallop any more and gets his kicks from observing young couples performing a threesome with his young wife.'

My expression obviously conveyed a negative response.

'But he pays a thousand dollars a session and the girl is a twenty-five year old beauty,' she pleaded.

Although this was a more than generous punting fee, with the magic Lloyd's underwriting pen of Goldfinger Posgate filling my coffers, I could afford moral outrage.

'I am sorry, my love; I don't mind a lusty romp, but not with some randy old Yankee goat looking up my arse.'

The mission did not proceed (not with my involvement, anyway!) and I am only relating the incident as it was an apt precursor to subsequent developments.

Every year in late November, my fellow marine brokers and I hosted a Christmas bash in the subterranean Plantation Restaurant just off Fenchurch Street. Guests at these gatherings were selected from the elite of the City underwriting fraternity plus a few of our more broad-minded clients.

As 'barrack room damages' often exceeded the bar bill, at the end of every party, the maître d', Izzy, would wobble his chins at me and vow, 'Last time, Mr Kemble-Clarkson!' Nevertheless, the following year's beano would find him obsequiously greeting everyone with his well-greased palms on his ample hips.

The party was always strictly a stag affair, but when I explained this to Rose she shook her head and gave me one of her dangerously mischievous glances.

'How sad. I can understand excluding wives and sweethearts, but I have got lots of hungry, stunning models on my books who would love to meet some of your well-heeled friends.'

As most of the attendees were philanderers to a greater or lesser degree, injecting some luscious ladies into the proceedings would certainly do no harm, so I went for it. Thus, half an hour into the 1972 Marine Christmas party, 20 scantily clad beauties were offered the season's greetings by our young (and not so young) lions of the City of London.

Very soon a good time was being had by all and the eventual pairing off was reminiscent of the graduation party staged by Lee Marvin in the classic war film, *The Dirty Dozen*.

Being the senior host, I did my best to ensure that the most important guests got the pick of the harem. I was, therefore, somewhat nonplussed when Peter Salt, a star attendee, could not be separated from Georgina, who happened to be a converted Greek sailor!

The very best of parties rarely run without a hitch and this one was no exception. Julia, the youngest 'model' present, had taken a shine to Jake Bond, one of our junior brokers. This cheeky chappy, who was to eventually achieve great things, was at this time sharing a flat with the depraved UFO pop group, so he was capable of anything.

Initially I was somewhat irritated by Jake's presumptuousness in mopping up the talent ahead of his elders and betters. However, he earned instant forgiveness on opting to perform a striptease with his new-found friend which would hopefully lead up to an inevitable conclusion!

As the couple disrobed to a Stones record they received a leery ovation with Jake's gyrating rear receiving special approval from Ronald Pool, a keenly bisexual underwriter. Then disaster struck. Julia slipped on some spilt beer and sat on a discarded glass which shattered, seriously lacerating her left buttock. The ensuing bleeding was profuse and it did not take the ranting of Izzy, who was still in shock over the nudity, to persuade us to phone for an ambulance.

Our 999 call unfortunately also triggered a visit from the City Constabulary which put the fear of God into many of our guests and temporarily destabilised the visiting nymphs. However, as soon as the paramedics had departed with a staunched Julia, the senior police officer present put his arm around the nearest female.

'So what about some Christmas cheer for the Old Bill, then?'

Following a few drinks and some cuddles, the boys in blue resumed their duties and the party swung on to its various conclusions, leaving Izzy to nurse his nervous breakdown.

As Rose's beau, I had deemed it prudent to avoid the more lascivious aspects of the evening. This had given me the opportunity to focus upon the bright pink cards that her girls were dishing out to the guests, which pronounced in gold lettering:

Broaden the circle of your friends with
THE NORMAN ROSE ESCORT AGENCY.
Just pick up the phone and you won't be alone.

At last the cat had fully emerged from the bag. From always having been a keen punter, I had now inadvertently become the City of London's first amateur pimp!

When the die is cast or, as some folks say, 'it is written', my normal philosophy is to accept the inevitable and make the most of it; which is precisely what I decided to do in this case.

Rose was patently relieved over my relaxed attitude towards her true occupation and readily fielded questions that my natural curiosity prompted. My probing revealed some fascinating information concerning the 'great and the good' following the Christmas soirée. For instance it appeared that, even though Georgina's sex change was not that extensive, Peter had improvised with admirable skill and imagination.

As our recent guests seemed to have had the time of their lives, a few weeks later I decided to cash in on the situation and take Rose on a tour of Lloyd's. Being a shameless extrovert, she was overjoyed at the offer and presented herself on the appointed day, suitably booted and mini-dressed in bottle green.

Until 1969 the presence of women in the Lloyd's dealing room was strictly taboo unless they were accompanied by a male member. This rule naturally led to a great deal of rather pathetic schoolboyish behaviour from brokers and underwriters whenever a female was escorted round the market. In his 1930s cartoon series on Lloyd's, the late Henry Mayo Bateman brilliantly captures this scenario in 'A Little Ray of Sunshine Visits Lloyd's'. The drawing depicts a swanky young fellow parading his lady friend through the underwriting room whilst traders with elongated necks and popping eyes ogle her. Even though, by then, the ban had been lifted, nothing much had changed and, as Rose and I passed through the hallowed precincts of Britain's largest invisible export, I am certain that Bateman would have been proud of us.

In addition to demonstrating appropriate interest in revered artefacts, such as the Lutine Bell, my lady conducted herself with the poise of a film star during personal introductions. En route to the Nelson Room, however, she did overdo things a tad by indulging in an Evita-style waving session from the balcony to the entire marine market.

During a brief tour of our great naval hero's memorabilia, Rose appeared to be especially interested in one particular display cabinet.

'What a fabulous person,' she suddenly remarked with great enthusiasm.

On acknowledging the superlative qualities of Britain's favourite admiral, I was regarded with incredulity.

'I was talking about Lady Hamilton, silly. You should read the letters instead of looking at the swords.'

I was loath to explain that the erstwhile courtesan had died nine years after Nelson in drunken penury, and suggested that we move on to Shorts, the favoured local lunch venue.

As we departed from Lloyd's, my little ray of sunshine was temporarily eclipsed by a streak of cloud. This was in the angular form of Rory Spencer, who overtook us and rudely blocked our passage at the exit door.

'You really are riding for a fall this time, Kemble-Clarkson,' he venomously intoned.

When I had decided on a career in Lloyd's, my dear father, who

had been a Baltic Exchange ship broker since the 1920s, gave me two sage pieces of advice: 'Always remember two vital factors during your working life. Firstly, that there is no such thing as a small enemy and, secondly, that the graveyards are full of indispensable people.'

It was the first axiom that I had unwisely ignored.

Rory was a generally unpopular underwriter. This was not due to the fact that he owed his senior position to nepotism, but because he specialised in extending the limits of crass offensiveness. We were contemporaries, and although I had managed to rise above his vulgarity for a long time, this had ended acrimoniously the previous year. The event had occurred at his market base when he had obscenely berated his deputy and me in public for a deal we had concluded whilst he was abroad. My red mist had instantly descended and I loudly suggested to his staff that it was high time for the nasty, grubby schoolboy to be taught a few manners. All the traders within earshot gave a whooping round of applause and, with a livid red face, Rory was obliged to beat an ignominious retreat.

My foe now obviously smelt an opportunity for retribution and, having regarded Rose with disdain, he fired a Parthian shaft as he strutted on his way.

'If you believe that you can get away with treating Lloyd's as your personal playground, you had better think again as I intend to cut you down to size.'

Flashing a half-hearted V sign, I ruefully recalled that Rory had recently been elected to the all-powerful Committee of Lloyd's. Father was right, and this was no small enemy!

As its ambience was decidedly seedy, the slipshod proprietors of Shorts Tavern relied heavily upon its close proximity to Lloyd's and the Baltic Exchange for patronage. Whilst the scuffed floor boards exuded the odour of stale beer, an array of stained prints on the walls failed to disguise the rotten state of the worm-eaten panelling. Furthermore, when customers descended to the cellar restaurant they faced the distinct possibility of sewage seepage via its algae-encrusted walls.

Nevertheless, it could not be denied that that the menu offered a selection of adequately prepared cuisine which was complimented by a first-class wine list. Thus the hostelry regularly attracted a throng of market traders and many weighty deals were negotiated within its shoddy environs.

Needlessly to say, on our arrival at this popular watering hole, Rose was in her element and pink cards proliferated as she effusively greeted her new fans.

To my bewilderment, I found that by the time we adjourned for lunch with some selected revellers, I was feeling distinctly ill at ease. Initially, I attributed this to my career-threatening fracas with Rory and it was not until we were well into the main course that I put my finger on it: I had lost the initiative. I suddenly realised that Rose was deigning to include me in *her* entertainment of *my* friends at *my* expense! Morosely convincing myself that I had become a sideshow to a siren, by the port and brandy stage I was willing the party to end.

I fielded comments from Ronald and other guests on my lack of customary bonhomie by pleading a migraine. Then, after what seemed an eternity of long-winded farewells, I bundled Rose into a taxi and we set off for Tedworth Square. I was in no mood for Pimlico and Norman's snide remarks.

By the time we reached our destination my mood had boiled us into our first real row, the details of which are too tedious to relate. 'Her Ladyship' did, however, get in a final dig.

'You accuse me of using you. What about that bitch up north that you have never stopped seeing, you bastard? With my connections, I should have had her fixed.'

Any feelings of guilt over this well-founded accusation were instantly dispelled by the vicious ruthlessness of Rose's threat. Although I tried to kid myself that this had just been jealous bravado, I knew that the lady's twilight occupation gave her access to some very unscrupulous people.

The next morning, in spite of our having kissed and made up, I still had the uncomfortable feeling that matters on the Rose front were definitely on the wane. I was, therefore, secretly relieved when she told me that, the following week, she was off to spend an extended Christmas vacation with her folks in Derry. The night before her departure we had a gift-swapping dinner at Waltons and went our separate ways.

I opted to spend the festive season with some close friends of mine,

John and Jeanette Downing, who worked in the fascinating Fleet Street media world. John was a senior press photographer whose intrepid exploits were to earn him an MBE, whilst Jeanette ran the classified advertisements section of a leading evening journal.

Every weekend their spacious home in Weybridge became a virtual kibbutz where any of their broad range of friends was welcome, provided that they brought refreshments.

On such occasions there was always much drinking, dancing and passionate debate, where I often got a pasting via being outnumbered by literati lefties. Water-borne pub crawls up the river in someone's boat often occurred, and nightly 'Forecast Whist' schools were obligatory.

The Christmas holiday followed the customary pattern and it was not until I was about to depart that Jeanette drew me aside and planted my feet firmly back on the ground.

'I really enjoyed meeting Rose the other week; she is a tremendous giggle and, as you know, her agency has a regular slot in my personal ads publication.'

My arm was squeezed to focus my wandering attention.

'Just before the break a senior Vice Squad officer paid me a visit in connection with my section of the paper. It would appear that the police are currently investigating procurement rackets and I was given a weeding out list which included your girlfriend's outfit. If Rose is dishing out her services to your business friends, Lloyd's is unlikely to be amused if a story breaks. Just watch it, darling, that's all.'

All this certainly came as quite a shock so, following a round of fond goodbyes with special thanks to Jeanette for not ruining my holiday earlier, I headed home post haste.

I had been warned, and so on arriving back at Tedworth Square, the first thing I did was try to get in touch with Rose in Derry. As with my earlier calls over the past week, the phone was answered by an evasive Irish woman who promised to pass on my message. This had so far failed to elicit any form of response and, somewhat ominously, no telephones were being answered at the Norman Rose office.

Fortunately, my dilemma was conveniently sidelined in early

January when I was sent on an urgent mission to New York which required following up in Hong Kong. However, I was much distracted during the trip by reports in the English newspapers listing certain personal contact organisations under investigation by the CID. As these included the Norman Rose Escort Agency, I was then dogged by a stream of phone calls which ranged between deep concern and blind panic. Nevertheless, much to my relief, by the time I got back to England all was 'quiet on the Western Front' and continued to be so.

It transpired via input from Jeanette that my sleepless nights had been unwarranted as the fuzz totally failed to locate anyone who had been involved with Rose's little enterprise.

Of equal importance, Rory's attempts to impugn my position at Lloyd's fell on stony ground. This was due to the fact that certain high-profile establishment figures who had availed themselves of the pink card services were reluctant to cast the first stone!

A long time was to pass before I was given the opportunity to tie up some irritating loose ends.

Almost three years later I was in the Churchill Hotel's lounge bar awaiting Fred Long, one of my American clients, when resurrection occurred.

It was the reminiscent sound of a throaty chuckle that attracted my attention, and I soon traced it to a nearby bar stool. Sure enough, there was Rose, sipping a glass of champagne with her arm around a nervous-looking young man.

Hoping that Fred would sustain his habit of always arriving late, I advanced and surprised my ex with a fond embrace that almost toppled her off her precarious perch. After she had recovered her somewhat tipsy composure and dispatched her coy escort to sort out dinner arrangements, we indulged in some merry memories. However, as my guest was likely to appear at any moment, I was keen to focus on something that had always bugged me.

'Rose, there is one thing that I must ask you, as I have always been certain that I had never set eyes on you before our Savoy meeting. How on earth did you get hold of my name and number?'

She chortled and took another sip of her drink. 'Shortly before we got together, do you remember picking up a slinky redhead at Nice airport?'

'Eh … Laura, an air hostess. We only had a couple of dates as I recall.'

'That's because you did not get your wicked way, I bet,' Rose chided.

I conceded the point, ruefully recalling some fraught moments.

'The lady was on the subsidiary section of my team that catered for alternative therapy. She hated men!'

I smiled as, even years later, I was relieved to learn this. However, my ex immediately torpedoed my libido recovery.

'Laura told me that she had been dating some flashy City bloke who seemed to have more money than sense. She then gave me your card as she thought that you might open up a lucrative area for expanding my business. Her assumption proved correct and the rest is history!'

Having accepted all this in good grace, I decided to extend my curiosity. 'Dare I ask how much money you managed to make from your corner of the service industry via the Norman Rose agency?'

Rose feigned deep cogitation. 'I was only asked to answer one question, Nigel but I reckon that during the year in which we got together, I pulled in about £113,000. My game is computer dating now!'

As this shattering response defied comment, with Fred waving at me and the callow youth returning, I decided that it was time for a final farewell to this incorrigible lady.

And so it came to pass that a twenty-one year old courtesan took on the establishment at their favourite game, amassed a fortune and made a monkey of yours truly!

8

La Double Philander

In order to ease executive stress, the City of London's institutions encourage their upper echelons to attend conferences and seminars regularly. In theory, the purpose of such gatherings is to create a relaxed forum for developing business strategies away from workaday pressures. In practice, the exotic locations commonly chosen for these 'getaways' tend to promote anything but commercial application. One of the most popular events in the marine insurance community's calendar has always been the Monte Carlo 'September Rendezvous', and I shall ever remember the 1972 event.

'So, I made it at last, Nige; an invitation to the greatest bonanza of the year. Does Monte Carlo mark a belated start to my meteoric career?

'Well, Chris, so long as you can weather temptation without putting your foot in it, this jaunt will do you no harm at all. There will be an army of clients and underwriters from all over the world for you to impress, but please leave wives, daughters and, especially, mistresses well alone. Your raunchier needs will be adequately catered for via naughty nightspots and enthusiastic amateurs.'

This exchange was with my new assistant Chris Went, whilst in flight bound for Nice to spend the following week sacrificing our health for the company.

I had met Chris via the Lloyd's community and we had become great bon viveur partners in crime during my well-timed period of bachelorhood between 1968 and 1974. Although he was always witty and charming company, his extreme affability tended to blunt the competitive edge which defines a successful businessman. However, as he brokered competently and clients liked him, I had decided to transgress the golden rule of not employing friends.

My chum's plump good looks lit up as a delectable trolley dolly plonked another complimentary cocktail in front of him.

'So, Nige, to assist me in not screwing up, give me a briefing on the cast of runners and riders that I am likely to encounter during the conference.'

I took a sip from my vodka and tonic as I pondered on the question.

'Well, top of the heap from the home team this year will be Rupert Wellington-Green who never misses this bash. By now, he will have wended his way down in easy stages, sharing the wheel of the Bentley Continental with his amiable thug of a chauffeur, Buster Brown.'

Chris cut in, 'That guy Rupert is one hell of a boss. When he interviewed me for the job, I was served a glass of champagne at ten a.m. whilst helping him choose a carnation for his buttonhole. He then discussed my sporting interests for half an hour and gave me the job, plus a great piece of advice ...'

I finished the sentence: 'It never matters what you do, so long as you do it with style.'

This axiom typified our chief to a tee, who was a good-looking, debonair Old Harovian with an Oxford boxing blue and a good war under his belt. Rupert prided himself on having scant knowledge of insurance but knowing how to pick people who did. He also knew exactly how to charm and manipulate the diverse team of characters with whom he surrounded himself, to forge a first-class operation. I was fortunate enough to be one of them.

'You will have noticed that our excitable Peter Pollard is flying with us with Rolf Farstud, an important but irascible Norwegian client who needs careful handling.'

A tense, gaunt face curtained by a mop of ginger hair peered around the seat back across the aisle in front of us.

'We heard that, Nigel. Just you make sure that you don't give me anything to get excited about, you wretched fellow. I don't know why I put up with your nonsense. You smoke like a chimney, you drink like a fish and also ...'

'Please, Peter. I cannot take all this publicity.'

Before I could say more, Rolf's cadaverous Nordic features

appeared over the top of the same row of seats, bearing a wintry smile. 'As Bente is not with me, at least my marriage has a chance of staying intact.'

He was alluding to an unfortunate incident which had occurred when I was sitting next to his wife at a Christmas dinner in Bergen the year before. I had not realised that the couple had just patched up a rift over Rolf's indiscretions with a Japanese lady. In order to make polite conversation, I had remarked to Bente how much I had enjoyed spending time with her husband in Tokyo earlier in the year. Thinking that I was taking the mickey, the lady had slapped my face and left the party in floods of tears, leaving behind a confused Nigel, an uncomfortable Rolf and a panicking Peter.

As the Punch and Judy show retreated behind its parapet, I became aware of my left arm being gently squeezed. The welcome instigator of this caress was an incredibly pretty and curvaceous blonde who was sitting across the aisle from me. Like all the other red-blooded male passengers, Chris and I had followed this lady's course through emigration to embarkation. Caution had prevailed, however, because, as she was very young to be in first class, we suspected that her middle-aged neighbour was either her father or a very fortunate sugar daddy.

'So what might your third vice be?' she drawled, her mischievous eyes fixing mine like deep blue shark-infested pools.

I smiled indulgently. 'Gambling, of course.' Then I whispered, 'Excuse our friends; they can't help it, one is bonkers and the other is not British.'

'Thank you so much, I happen to be a foreigner too.'

I was taken aback. 'Well, you sure could have fooled me. When did Chelsea declare independence?'

She simpered coquettishly. 'Blame Roedean. Actually, I am Swedish but you are forgiven as you and your friend have been saying nice things about my stepdaddy. We must all be bound for the same "jolly", as he calls it. It is great to meet you Nigel; Mummy has told me all about you and I am sure that we will have lots of fun during the week.'

Not if I have anything to do with it, I thought, as I realised to whom I was talking. A number of years back, Rupert had dumped his wealthy harridan of a first wife in favour of a beautiful Swedish model. Although I knew Gunilla well, I had never met either of her daughters, of whom this was obviously the elder.

'Then you must be Elsa. Do meet Chris Went, Rupert's newest recruit.'

'Hi, Elsa, I was wondering when I might be permitted to join the party. If I had had the sense to grab the aisle seat, we would have broken the ice far sooner.'

I was strangely and illogically relieved that Chris's little flirt inspired nothing more than a cool nod and a remote smile.

'Well, boys, let's all take full advantage of the free champagne to celebrate solving our identity crisis.'

Although it soon became clear that her pertinacity exceeded her intellect, Elsa proved to be a lively companion for the rest of the short flight. Fortunately, Peter and Rolf chose to rise above our carousing. In fact, they did not acknowledge our young companion until Rupert introduced her to them at the airport when he met our arriving plane.

The boss was in high spirits and insisted that we all meet up for a bevy in the lofty village of Eze en route to Monaco.

'Afraid that I can't squeeze everyone into the Bentley so you two will have to make your own way.'

'No problem, Sir; I have a Hertz car waiting.'

My mentor gave me a look of mock severity. 'Well, as long as it does not put my banger to shame, that's OK.' Then to no one in particular, 'Would you believe it? This saucy young devil's July expenses exceeded mine. Outrageous!'

As he laughed and punched me in the ribs playfully, I ruefully recalled that jocularity had not featured in my reprimand for this infringement.

'It's only a small Renault convertible.'

'Good, we will see you at the Bar des Oiseaux, then.'

Peter gave me an ingratiating smile and a wave as he and Rolf boarded the elegant transport. He was very well aware that, after my ardently Roman Catholic father disowned me for my trespasses, Rupert had come to regard me as the son he never had.

During the brief scenic drive to Eze, the best views that Chris and

I witnessed were the batteries of bare-breasted beauties boosting their bank balances on boats!

'Sorry not to have completed my cast briefing but I am afraid it was pre-empted by events.'

Chris flinched as I negotiated the extreme edge of a sharp bend on a precipitous stretch of the coast road.

'For f***'s sake, Nige, when will you ever learn not to look at people you are talking to whilst you are driving? I am certain that I shall be able to play out the week by ear, thanks. You are the one who should watch it; Elsa spells trouble and she is headed in your direction.'

'Then I shall brush her off like the child that she is.' I almost convinced myself.

When we arrived at our towering destination, having parked the car in a narrow 45-degree village lane, we located our party on the Oiseaux terrace. With a wonderful view of the coast and yacht-flecked azure sea the Eze location was, indeed, idyllic. This was in spite of the *merde de oiseau* competing with the *merde de taureau* emanating from the patrons around the tables.

I was pleased to observe that Marino de Caldo, with whom I shared responsibility for our Genoese operation, had joined our table. Exquisitely charming and boyishly handsome beyond his years, this member of the Italian minor aristocracy was the epitome of sophistication. Like an Oscar Wilde leading man, instead of sweating, Marino just glowed iridescently. When a penniless war refugee, he had traded his class for brass by marrying a shipowner's daughter who adored him in spite of his serial philandering. On asking him one day if wearing his wedding ring on a chain around his neck was due to an allergy, I was regarded in astonishment.

'Nigel, how naive you are: it is because by the time the ladies discover that I am married, it is too late!'

Despite having lived in London for 20 years, Marino ever maintained his dulcet 'mamma mia' accent. This was not only to titillate the fair sex, but also to capitalise upon the patronising generosity that we tend to shower upon those not fortunate enough to be born British.

I had barely finished greeting Marino when the stocky, white-suited

REFLECTIONS OF A RASCAL

figure of Paulo Travata oiled up to our table, leering at us through the eye which lacked a black silk patch. Sadly, this remarkably able senior director of the Fiat insurance arm had never come to terms with his roots. Nobody had let him forget that, in the late 1940s, Roberto Agnelli had employed him on a whim whilst Paulo was serving him as a young steward during a train journey.

'Buongiorno everyone, welcome to the Italian colonies. Rupert, you are looking more distinguished than ever and, Marino, your ladies get progressively younger, and more beautiful.'

As he drew Elsa's hand to his lips, Rupert's contempt for the ageing popinjay bubbled to the surface. 'That happens to be my daughter whose hand you are slobbering over. Now you must excuse me, Paulo; I have things to discuss with my staff.'

As the boss grabbed my arm and propelled me towards the indoor bar area, the Italian Cyclops called after us. 'Arrivederci Rupert, I suppose you are encouraging young Nigel to steal more business from his betters.'

Ignoring the crass remark, we passed into the inner sanctum and, having ordered two Negronis, we settled into a convenient alcove.

'Sorry to drag you off like that, but I need to ask a personal favour of you.'

As Rupert's intense but kindly blue eyes bored into mine with more than a hint of urgency, I effected a half-serious expression of manly resolve as I held his gaze.

'I am honoured, sir, and will do my damnedest to serve your needs.'

He instantly burst into laughter. 'I can't stand you when you are not being cocky. You make such a lousy Sir Galahad.' Then, reverting to his more sombre mode, 'It's Elsa. Her mother, who adores her, has sprung her on me for the week. If she gets mixed up with any of these greasy ice cream salesmen like Paulo, there will be all hell to pay. In a nutshell, I want you to be her lord protector. I know that, like most girls of her generation, she is probably a nympho, but Gunilla perceives her as an innocent lamb. What do you say?'

'Well, Rupert, if Mummy is so concerned about her daughter's cherry, how come she has sent her off to this den of iniquity?'

A look of resignation flickered across the rugged countenance.

'Well spotted, you young devil. The truth is that she could be here as a watchdog to hamstring my usual Monte Carlo activities, with which you are familiar.'

'So this has nothing to do with Elsa's sexual security. You are asking me to take the heat off you, Rupert.'

'That's about the size of it, and I trust you to behave like a gentleman and take no licentious advantages. Are you on, or not?'

There is only one sensible response to an offer you cannot refuse. 'Of course I am delighted to oblige, sir, but in view of your understandable moral caveat, permanent surveillance is out of the question. You will have to let me know when you are seeking a clandestine moment.'

'Actually, Nigel, I have an assignation on a yacht in the harbour tonight. If you would escort Elsa into town, check her in at the hotel and sort out some supper, that would be most helpful. Take that charming new fellow along as well, it looks more respectable.'

So there I was, stitched up like a kipper!

Following a couple more drinks on the terrace, where the ranks had swelled to an international throng, Elsa, Chris and I took our leave. Having left a metallic paint farewell imprint on the parking spot's granite wall, we cautiously wended our way to champagne city.

Although Monte Carlo's palm court splendour had become somewhat tarnished by the early 1970s, the Hotel de Paris still clung on to something of its former glory. On our arrival, the overplanted foyer was awash with babbling conference delegates who displayed the bright-eyed anticipation of children released for school holidays.

Our registration immediately became delayed by many 'bees' with whom I was acquainted buzzing around the 'honeypot' at my side. On our being eventually checked in by a gay desk clerk with a goose quill pen who had the audacity to display disapproval at Elsa's merry state, I decided that it was time to assert my authority.

'You two are on the third floor and I am on the fifth. Elsa, you are decidedly squiffy so, as it is already nine thirty p.m., I would suggest that you take advantage of room service and then grab an early night. Chris, we have a late supper appointment with Ernst Von Staalhein at the Tiptop Bar down the road. He is a pain in the arse, but his dad's account helps pay your wages. Let's unpack and get sorted, then I will see you back down here in twenty minutes.'

'You are not casting me off like a well-worn boot; I am coming too, so there,' our charge protested.

I could not be bothered to debate the issue and, thankfully, in spite of her protestation, we were not destined to see any more of the young lady that night.

Moments later, I was weaving my way along a gilded corridor to room 512, when I ran into the squat form of Leone Marco, who appeared to have emerged from the *chambre* next door. The louche but lovable bearded rascal who was our man in Genoa gave me a big hug.

'So, Nigel my dear, you got here in one piece for a change.'

Being the son of a Jewish ship chandler from Odessa, Leone worked too hard at being an Italian gentleman, so he found it difficult to come to terms with my rumbustious behaviour.

I laughed as he smoothed his YSL shirt and used a silk handkerchief to buff the scuffing that I had inflicted on a Gucci loafer during our embrace.

'Oops. Sorry, old boy. So you are my next-door neighbour for the week; what fun.'

'No, I am on the sixth floor, number 672. I just came down to look for you,' was the somewhat defensive reply. I was certain that I had just seen him exit room 514. Strange, but hardly worth pursuing.

My little friend suddenly started rubbing his hands together in obvious agitation. 'Please unpack and smarten yourself up quickly, Nigel. Rupert, you and I should meet at the Tiptop Bar in fifteen minutes. Michele D'Emperio is buying us dinner.'

'Since when? I am afraid that is out of the question, my hairy hound. Apart from the fact that I can't stand your mafioso monkey, Rupert is bonking on a boat somewhere and Chris Went and I have another date.'

I thought Leone would burst into tears. 'My dear, just because Michele is Sicilian does not automatically make him a member of the Cosa Nostra. You know that we have the Cosida deal pending and I telexed you about this meeting last week. Sometimes I think that your wild life is addling your brain. You and Chris can bring your guest along as well and I will pick up the bill, but please get a move on, I beg you.'

As he beetled off down the passageway, I remembered how much he loathed Ernst's schlager-scarred arrogance, and called after him, 'Our guest is your least favourite storm trooper: Von Staalhien.'

Leone stopped in his tracks and regarded me mercurially. 'In that case we will just have to see how the Gestapo gets on with the Mafia; business is business!'

Within 20 minutes I was showered, changed and, after a quick Scotch from the minibar, ready for anything. As I rushed out of the door, much to my surprise, I ran into Barton Bendish who seemed to be loitering outside the increasingly intriguing room 514. This rather shop-soiled Adonis was a notorious Lloyd's roué who seemed to make plenty of money out of doing nothing in particular.

'Barton, what are you hanging around here for? Up to no good, I'll be bound.'

'Nigel; great to see you. I was just about to light up as I passed through.' With undue haste, he removed a Marcovitch Black Russian from an expensive-looking cigarette case. 'Sorry, would you like one too? Must go; late for a date. See you soon.'

With that, he was off, leaving me to inhale one of his flashy lung-liners.

When I got to the lifts, who should emerge but Percy Sprag, Barton's great friend and alleged partner in the art of gregarious copulation.

'Percy, you just missed your chum. I shall have to be on my mettle if I am sharing a floor with you two!'

The ageing poltroon looked a trifle uncomfortable. 'Don't worry; this hotel is out of our league, we are just going to a party. *A tout à l'heure*, Nigel.'

Whilst he scuttled off down the corridor, it occurred to me that, as his crony had just made a great show of leaving, the 'party' was obviously a highly clandestine affair.

The rest of the evening turned out to be a delightful disaster, which began with the ill-conceived Tiptop get-together. Oil and water had a better chance of blending than a 6 foot 4 inches self-opinionated Prussian, an insecure Italian Israelite and a neurotic Sicilian midget. Disharmony was exacerbated when Ernst made it abundantly clear that he disapproved of the Latins repeatedly chattering together in their own lingo.

Barely an hour had passed before Leone pulled me to one side in desperation. 'Nigel, this is impossible. You keep laughing, which means that you are tipsy, Chris is talking rubbish, and that drunken Nazi shit is being most insulting. Michele is livid and threatening to withdraw his business.'

At this, it was my turn to have a sense of humour failure. 'Listen, he won't find anyone else who is capable of negotiating his crap and he can't even pay his premiums on time. I reckon Michele needs me more than I need him.'

Leone wisely abandoned his aggrieved stance. 'All right, my dear, you are probably right, but please don't get cross. However, I do think that I should take him off to dinner before this gets really ugly.'

I agreed, so, after stilted farewells, Ernst, Chris and I repaired to the Café de Paris where, following delicious canapés and excellent wine, I soon got into my choral mode. We were well into 'Aboard the Good Ship Venus', when the only patron who was not appalled by our bawdy renditions plonked herself down at our table.

Blanche was 60 if she was a day. Nevertheless, her body, which was sheathed in a clinging red silk cocktail dress and festooned with priceless gold and diamond jewellery, was in very reasonable shape. Although the visible areas of her epidermis were overseasoned by solar exposure, beneath her lived-in countenance, a fine bone structure was still evident. Framed by a richly coiffeured mane of silver-blonde hair, her slightly bloodshot green eyes lit up as she joined in with the final chorus of our sea shanty.

Regrettably, her aura of elegance was instantly shattered when she opened her mouth and revealed a rusty Brooklyn accent that you could have cut with a knife.

'OK yous guys, I'm Blanche. My turn to teach you to sing a couple of Yankee numbers. Where are you all from?'

We identified ourselves.

'Well, Brits I adore. Krauts I hate, they killed my third husband so Ernie, you can f*** off!'

Chris and I had no problem with this suggestion as it was high time to jettison this tediously sozzled member of the master race. However, as Ernst staggered cursing from the restaurant, having

failed in an attempt to click his heels, a profusely agitated maître d'
appeared at our table.

'Madame et messieurs, Your singing and swearing is upsetting our
other guests so, regrettably, I must ask you to settle up and depart
immediately.'

The only immediacy which occurred was Blanche's brilliant
response. 'How dare you address us in that fashion, Marcel. Listen,
you got two options. Either you bring a complimentary bottle of your
best champagne to our table or I buy this joint and fire your ass!'

Champagne was promptly served without further ado and we
were soon to learn why via a subsequent colourful conversation. It
transpired that Blanche spent every summer in the principality and
was something of a local institution. Apparently, she had been
married six times to increasingly wealthy spouses, the last of whom
had been a Saudi prince whom she touchingly described thus: 'Best
piece of ass I ever had; f***ed like a stallion!'

Buying the Café de Paris would probably have been well within the
financial capability of our outlandish new friend. However, as we
quaffed complimentary bubbly, I observed some important Japanese
clients being seated nearby. Thus, when Blanche insisted that we
burst into song again, I suggested that it was time to move on.

'Wait a minute; I think that we should give old "happy crappy" a
break and have a flutter at the Casino.'

My ploy worked, and an inconvenient affront to fragile Oriental
sensibilities was averted.

'That is the greatest idea I heard all evening. Hey "happy crappy",
check please.'

Blanche had obviously thoroughly enjoyed her persecution of the
hapless maître d'. So much so that she was unable to stop cackling
and chortling, as she linked arms with Chris and me whilst we
covered the short distance to the world's most famous gambling den.

Of all the vices, wagering has never been near the top of my list
of fun ways to blow your money. Nevertheless, this pastime became
far more attractive on a business trip when, within reason, whilst you
retained your winnings, losses were down to the company.

When we arrived at the casino, I was all for playing blackjack as I
have always deluded myself that the game requires a modicum of

skill. Blanche was having none of it, though; her target was the main roulette hall and, after she had cashed up chips to a value of the average British annual wage, that is where we ended up.

Whilst Chris and I moderately abused corporate expenses, our vintage vamp was racking up a small fortune through what she assured us was her infallible system. Then, when for the first time, play ended totally *sans gagner* for Blanche, altercation struck with a vengeance. As the traditionally phlegmatic croupier collected the losing chips, she sprang to her feet like a cobra ready to strike.

'Hey Mac, you raked in my winning stake: dix-sept. I was on dix-sept which was the winning noomero, you blind punk.'

The stolid little official ignored her like the idle wind as he continued to consolidate the bank's haul.

'Hey, shithead; you got cloth ears? You just stole nearly a thousand bucks from me! What do you propose to do about it?'

When the target of Blanche's abuse continued to register in-difference, her vitriol erupted dramatically. Having violently kicked over a gold-trimmed velvet chair, she strode around the gaming table to confront her provocateur. Unbelievably, the blow that she then delivered to his sullen countenance, which matched many that I have received in the square ring, barely wobbled his chins. With amazing stoicism the stocky arbiter slowly rose from his throne and returned the compliment with a swift uppercut. The hush that fell over the room as Blanche reeled back, clutching her jaw in shock and disbelief, proved to be the calm before the storm. Grabbing a neatly stacked plastic fortune, she hurled the counters into her opponent's sweating face. Then, before he had time to recover, she launched herself at him like a savage panther and knocked him to the floor. As security guards endeavoured to restrain the onslaught, my friend and I joined the general exodus, which included a number of familiar Lloyd's faces.

'Chris, I think that this lady is more than capable of taking care of herself, so we can make a discreet withdrawal with a clear conscience.'

We paused on emerging into the balmy Monaco night.

'Bloody hell, Nige, what a fruitless evening for crumpet. An untouchable teenager and a nutty geriatric.'

Chris gave me a quizzical look. 'Would you have done, though?'

I feigned intensely serious consideration. 'Only if she had asked me nicely.'

'No danger there, then,' was the jocular reply.

I would emphasise at this point that, if anything, my version of this extraordinary incident is understated. Although I was not destined to meet Blanche again, she ever lives in my memory as one of the most delightfully outrageous women that I have ever encountered.

As it was after 2 a.m. by the time we arrived back at the hotel, I opted to end the day whilst I was still ahead and grab an early night. The way to hell is paved with good intentions!

On returning to my room, I found that a small envelope with my name upon it in childish italics had been pushed under the door. It contained an unwelcome message:

> *When you read this don't be annoyed,*
> *We have to face what we can't avoid.*
> *How could you abandon me like that?!*
> *E. XXX.*

135

As I read the note, I suddenly became irritated with myself, not only for being flattered but also for feeling excited by its content. However, having swiftly dispelled lascivious fantasies, within ten minutes I was tucked up in bed and fast asleep from the moment my head touched the pillow.

Oblivion was not destined to last for long, however, which was evidenced by my luminous bedside clock when I awoke with a start at 3 a.m. As I grappled with enforced emergence from alcoholic somnolence, the source of the intrusion gradually became manifest.

From the banging, yelling and trilling of a doorbell, it became apparent that there was a man in the corridor outside who was less than happy. Hurriedly donning a courtesy robe, I rushed out and was not too surprised to discover that the focal point of the rumpus was room 514. What did shock me was the spectre from the past who was responsible.

'Good God, Tony, it just had to be you. Still an expert at raising the dead in the middle of the night, I see.'

Two bloodshot eyes focused unsteadily in a confusion of gradual recognition. 'Nigel, you old devil; it's been far too long. I am here representing the Hamilton Re, what's your excuse?'

Even though a suntan complimented his blond locks, Tony Cornell's physique had grossly deteriorated since our revels in the mid-1960s. His broad-belted, flared jeans and Regency-collared shirt failed to conceal a pot belly and an extra chin. I had witnessed the sad beginnings of Tony's decline when wine had turned to powder, women had frequently let him down and song had become an irrelevance.

He had, however, attempted to reinvent himself by joining the City's émigrés to Bermuda where insurance companies were being set up as honeytraps for the rich and greedy.

'Well, Tony, all I can say is that I am a little further up the ladder in the same shop, earning a crust and having a ball. More importantly, why are you making such a bloody racket when I am trying to sleep?'

As if in response to my question, the mystery room's door opened to the extent of its security chain and a female voice with a guttural French accent spoke angrily from within.

'How many times must I tell you to get lost, you swine? If you do not f*** off immediately, I shall call security.'

My erstwhile friend responded venomously. 'Go ahead, you bitch. I will tell them that you are a hooker and they will chuck you out. I shall also report you to the Gendarmes for deliberately crushing my thumb in your door.'

Nursing his obviously damaged hand, Tony suddenly lunged forward menacingly, with which, the portal slammed shut.

I had now witnessed more aggression in the past two hours than I had experienced since leaving the Army. Was there a full moon or could there be something in the water?

'For Christ's sake Tony, this reminds me of Tooting seven years ago when I had to rescue Sonja from one of your crazed rages. Be a good chap, calm down and go home. I will catch up with you during the week.'

I managed to propel my former friend towards the lifts.

'Sorry, Nigel, you are right. I am staying at Les Ambassadors; room seventy. Give me a bell and we can meet for a drink and catch up.'

As Cornell meandered off, I recalled how, in his heyday, he used to love appearing at Lloyd's sporting the 'as removed' knickers of his latest conquest as a top pocket handkerchief.

'Fine, Tony, I will definitely be in touch. Meanwhile, get that war wound fixed or you won't be hitching any more lifts!'

I returned to my room to discover that I was locked out. 'Shit, I could have sworn that I left the latch protruding to prevent this,' I muttered to myself. Having then set out for the floor's house phones, I was hailed by the newly identified tones of my next-door neighbour.

'Hey, Nigel, where are you off to? I want to thank you for rescuing me from that dreadful man.'

I turned and, leaning against the door jamb of room 514, the source of the voice was revealed. The lady in question was no classic beauty as she was rather short and slightly plump. Nevertheless, she still retained the magnetism of youth, complimented by excellent legs and fine breasts, all of which were barely concealed beneath her diaphanous red negligee.

'As a knight errant, it was all in a night's work. I do seem to have locked myself out, though.'

Doing her best to tidy up her bobbed auburn hair, she beckoned to me with a quizzical look in her large hazel eyes.

'My name is Bernadette and I come from Switzerland. Why not use my phone to get a spare key sent up?'

I was not to enter my room again until lunchtime.

Having left Bernadette to resume the pursuit of her calling, I was enjoying a Paradise cocktail in the main hotel bar when Chris Went intruded upon my recuperative interlude.

'I trust your resurrection follows an erection which led to a connection with a girl of good complexion who was free of all infection! Thanks a bunch for lumbering me with your ward who, rather surprisingly, seems devastated by your disappearance. What on earth is that red gunge that you are drinking? It looks like mouthwash.'

'Have you quite finished, Chris? In spite of your saucily presumptive repartee, my recent whereabouts are none of your business and I consider it rather sad that you can't amuse a teenager without my assistance. Also, if you had a modicum of sophistication, you would recognise that this "gunge" is the Hotel de Paris's special livener, Paradise juice; Paradise *perdu*, if you are not careful. Do try one. Meanwhile, where is that wretched girl?'

'She forgot her costume and had to make a phone call. We are off to have lunch at the Beach Club. Why don't you join us?'

As we sipped our red 'gunge', I regaled Chris with the general circumstances of my disappearance. We were just getting stuck into our second round when we were interrupted by an obviously riled Elsa.

'Judas! Chris and I have been phoning you to no avail all morning. Where have you been, you dirty stop-out?'

'I took a couple of sleeping pills so that I could be all bright-eyed and bushy tailed for you today.'

'Is that the best you can do, Nigel? Why didn't you just hold your calls? Anyway, as Daddy now seems to have vanished, let's have a super lunch and enjoy the seaside.'

Little that occurred during the afternoon was either super or enjoyable. For a start, Le Requin Complet, my favourite restaurant on the point, was fully booked. When bribery failed to secure a table, we were obliged to eat at a lesser, more public venue by the *plage* and next to the main swimming pool. This meant that our repast was repeatedly interrupted by other delegates with whom I was acquainted who were passing by.

The pushiest intruder was Dr Ho Sun Yu from the Dae Hoon Insurance Company in Korea who calmly invited himself to lunch. As he had shown me some memorable nights out in Seoul and was probably underfunded for Monaco, I was happy to include him. As usual, he looked just like a diminutive version of Goldfinger's Oddjob and insisted on doing his party trick, which I always found was corny enough to be funny. Without waiting to be introduced, he would walk up to people that he had never met before, grab their hand and bow solemnly, intoning, 'I am Dr Yu, who are you?'

As the little fellow was a highly qualified nuclear physicist, what he was doing in the insurance industry was a total mystery. However, behind his quaint Pidgin English smokescreen, he was an adroit operator and always great fun to be with.

Ho Sun's presence at our table obviously failed to impress a passing Japanese contingent as they then considered all Koreans to be savages. Billy Yagiu, a close friend of mine from Tokyo, beckoned me over for a brief word.

'Nigelsan, we go to special Requin Complet restaurant for lunch but, with your guest, you cannot go there. Glad to see that your girl friend from casino looks much younger in sunlight.'

As the yellow conformists filed off in order of seniority I realised that these interruptions could prove to be a blessing in disguise. At least they were frustrating Elsa's grudgingly welcome, but far too public, attempts to become overfamiliar. However, following my every move was shortly to land her in some cold water which became infinitely hotter for me with her stepfather.

During port and brandies after lunch, Elsa and I challenged Chris and Ho Sun to a table tennis contest. Although the squat Korean proved remarkably nimble, Chris managed to let him down badly. In the euphoria of our three to one victory, my partner and I smashed down the remnants of our drinks and fondly embraced.

Before allowing myself to get overexcited, I broke free and, playfully sprinting to the adjacent pool, I jumped in with Elsa in hot pursuit. Not realising that we were entering the water at the shallow end, much to everyone's horror she performed a perfect swallow dive. She was fortunate not to have broken her neck and, as it was, the blood that pumped out of the crown of her head as she surfaced caused major panic in the vicinity. Whilst Ho Sun bounced around like a yoyo, Chris and I swam over to assist the lifeguard in getting our casualty to a nearby first aid hut.

It was at this moment that, clad in sweat-stained tennis gear, Rupert and Peter Pollard chose to appear. Having attempted to comfort Elsa, who initially seemed remarkably unfazed, the boss's grim focus ominously swung in my direction.

'So this is how you entertain my daughter, Nigel. She reeks like a brewery, which is obviously why she has had this dreadful accident. How dare you give her too much to drink.'

Coming from Rupert, this was unjust if not downright hypo-critical. However, as I did not wish to jeopardise my comfortable existence, I backed off with profuse apologies.

Peter, of course, could not resist the temptation of sticking his oar in. 'Quite right too, Rupert. Nigel really is most irresponsible at times. I think that we are far too soft with him.'

Oddly enough, this snide remark did me no harm at all as I knew that Rupert secretly despised Peter for the obsequious toad that he was. Anyway, his trouble-making ceased when, suddenly realising that she had sustained more than a scratch, Elsa burst into a paroxysm of sobbing. Paramedics swiftly bundled her into the club's stand-by ambulance and she was rushed off for treatment with her stepfather in attendance.

Late Sunday evening found me attempting to relax on the upper deck of the yacht, *Il Bel Sogno*, as I reflected upon how the day had turned out to be anything but a beautiful dream.

My fellow guests were barely speaking to me. Rupert, who had left Elsa in hospital for overnight observation, was still smouldering. Leone continued to have the vapours over my upsetting his vacuous Sicilian gnome. Even Marino was being atypically offhand, as he occupied the room opposite mine and was unfairly blaming me for disturbing his beauty sleep the night before.

The hundred-foot vessel on which we were being entertained had been constructed from oak during the 1930s, in the days when cost was never allowed to prejudice luxury. The delicately carved fixtures and fittings were trimmed with gleaming brass and you could have happily eaten your lunch off the pristine engine room floor. She belonged to Tostalino Tankers SA, whose dynastic rulers were our hosts for the evening.

Whilst the three sons, Bepe, Maurizzio and Adriana, made it plain that they regarded insurance people as pond life, their father Alberto seemed to be genuinely delighted over the money we had saved him. How this wily old bear had managed to spawn three jackasses who had inherited nothing more than his good looks, God knows.

Sadly, as Papa had all the brains but spoke very little English, despite an idyllic setting, the evening had all the makings of a crashing bore. Fortunately, this did not prove to be entirely the case and the first event to relieve monotony occurred during dinner. We were all seated in the ornate dining salon with liveried flunkies poised behind each chair, when Bepe sat forward and beamed smugly at everyone around the table.

'So how do you like the Mouton Rothschild?'

Without batting an eyelid, Marino dazzlingly replied, 'It is a great year but it is corked.'

As the old man had a violent coughing attack, I have never seen glasses disappear from a table so swiftly or a wine steward look more devastated. I was convinced that, after we had left, he was probably keel-hauled attached to his cup chains.

When dinner was over, we were sitting on deck under the stars with cigars and brandies, staring at one another in stilted silence when Roberto suddenly stood up. Having smiled broadly at everyone, he raised his arms above his head and, beating time like a brass band conductor, he started to sing.

> *It's a long way to Tipperary,*
> *It's a long way to go.*
> *It's a long way to Tipperary,*
> *To the sweetest girl I know.*

Goodbye Piccadilly, farewell Leicester Square.
It's a long, long way to Tipperary
But my heart lies there.

One glance from Father was sufficient to ensure instant support from his scions whilst the rest of us joined in lustily and went on to support a selection of similar renditions. As, until Il Duce had been ventilated and hung out to dry beside his mistress, Italy was a German ally, this was a bizarre forum for British Army songs. Nevertheless, by the time we had 'packed up our troubles in our old kit bags' for departure, everyone was in high spirits and the best of friends.

Unfortunately, due to a typically Italian scenario, our love affair with the Tostalino family was to prove short-lived.

In common with many men, Leone, for all his posturing as a serious business man, suffered from not having sufficient blood in his body to service his brain and penis simultaneously! Unbeknown to any of us, he embarked on a passionate affair with Maria Grazzia Malfi, who just happened to be Adriana Tostalino's fiancée. Apparently, Leone was able to offer certain bedchamber skills which were found wanting in her spouse elect.

I was not to discover this until I was investigating the loss of the account the following year. However, before I could lay my hands on the little human tampon with castration as my minimum intent, there was an amazing turn of events. Papa Tostalino, his three sons and their finance director Dottore Zicca, were all arrested, convicted and jailed for tax irregularities. As all the family assets were then frozen, losing the business saved us from a very nasty bad debt situation.

Not surprisingly, Leone insisted that his indiscreet fling had been instigated so that he could monitor the shipowner's increasingly precarious standing. Furthermore, as a result of what he discovered, he had deliberately let the account go and saved us all a fortune. Showing his darker side, he then wickedly speculated what might be happening to 'pretty boy' Adriana's rear end in an Italian jail.

Quelle affaire!

Elsa arrived back from the hospital on Monday morning and the fact that Rupert had asked me to visit her with him boded well at court.

Because of possible concussion, the medics had decreed that our tempestuous young casualty should be kept out of the sun and rest up for the day. When I preceded Rupert into her darkened room, she squealed with delight and grabbed both my hands as I kissed her on the nose.

'Oh Nigel, now you are here you must stop Daddy from being such a big bully. He says that I have to lie here all day and miss all the fun. I refuse to be treated like a Vestal Virgin.

Little fear of that, I thought to myself.

The Monaco doctors had certainly made an artistic job of Elsa's cranial petit point. With her hair strategically arranged, the sutured gash in the top of her skull was barely visible and, as her blue eyes sparkled at me, she looked good enough to eat.

'Sorry, but like your father, I have to echo doctors' orders. Relax totally today and we can make up for it during the rest of the week.'

The boss broke his indulgent silence. 'Steady on, Nigel, with the medication she has been put on, booze is definitely taboo.'

Further comment was pre-empted by the doorbell's summons. Whilst Rupert went to answer it, my hands were impetuously seized once again.

'Phooey to that. But you will come back and share my siesta with me this afternoon, won't you?'

I was somewhat taken aback by the obvious proposition which I tried to believe was as a result of her blow to the head. As Rupert returned to the bedroom, unwelcomely accompanied by Pollard, I quickly whispered, 'Sorry, out of the question; meeting with the Japanese.'

Instantly releasing my hands, she pouted petulantly whilst her new visitor shuffled up to her bed as if she were a plague victim.

'Hi, Elsa, I just popped in on the offchance. My my, but we are looking down in the dumps. I do hope that you feel better than you look. Hullo, Nigel, come to survey your handiwork?'

Rupert put his hand on Peter's shoulder. 'Come on, old chap, there is no need for that kind of attitude. What on earth is the matter with you? On a fully funded jolly, you are supposed to be enjoying yourself.'

With my carrot-headed antagonist now subdued, we sat round Elsa's bed, failing to be either funny or comforting, like most people are when they visit the sick! As there were too many provocative glances spiced with innuendo flying in my direction, I was relieved when, after 20 minutes, Rupert stood up to signal departure.

'OK, darling, we will leave you to relax now but, never fear, I shall be on hand in the hotel and contactable through reception. I will pop in to see you this afternoon; meanwhile, take your pills and try to get some sleep.'

Having made our farewells, once we were out in the corridor the boss turned to me. 'You heard that, Nigel; no poolside lunch for you today. We shall have to entertain your American client in the terrace restaurant downstairs. At least we shall be outside but I trust that Lee will not be bringing his lush of a wife along.'

'If she is with him at the conference, I doubt if he will have the balls not to,' I replied.

Peter stopped in his tracks. 'If there is any chance of Bridget Derbyshire being present, count me out. Last time I met her she kept touching me up.'

'I hadn't realised that she could get that drunk,' I unkindly rejoined.

I was swiftly brought to heel. 'Now will you please cut that nonsense out, Nigel. If Peter does not wish to attend, invite the new chap in his place, unless he is off boozing it up at the Beach Club.'

'No, Rupert, he is in the hotel's Rainbow Room at a champagne reception promoting Bermuda's insurance industry. I will round him up.'

'Very well. Peter, you can bugger off and Nigel, I will see you and Christopher at the main bar in an hour's time at twelve forty-five. Book a table on the terrace and organise Lee and "Virginia Woolf" to join us at one. Do not be late.'

Having carried out my orders, I wandered along to the Bermudian party to seek out Chris and grab some free champagne. Having fought my way through a press of babbling delegates, I was not pleased when I discovered my assistant in deep conversation with Tony Cornell.

'Hey, Nigel, have your ears been burning? I have been telling your young friend all about the good old days.'

'Don't believe a word of it, Chris. Where do I get some bubbly?'

Tony put his moist hand on my shoulder. 'I am your Rainbow host, so please leave that detail to me.'

Whilst he moved off to rustle up some service, I quickly briefed Chris on his imminent luncheon assignment.

'Out of the question, old boy, I have just pulled a real beaut who works for the Munich Re and we are off to the beach for a grown-up picnic.'

As I was in no mood to argue, it was time to get tough. 'Then cancel her. This is a royal command and, although you may presently be in a silver champagne bucket, you are still just an oily rag. Furthermore, we must lose this guy as soon as possible; he is bad news. I know that he is my friend from the past but he was mainly just a drinker then. It is obvious that he has already been on the Charlie and is getting into one of his unpredictable paranoid moods.'

Looking suitably chastened by his reprimand, Chris nodded ruefully. 'Nail on the head, Nige. He has been sticking to me like shit to a blanket for the past half-hour and was starting to become a real pain in the arse. When our champagne arrives, let's split up, mingle with the throng and lose him.'

It was a sound plan, but easier said than done. Having escaped from our parasite whilst he was chatting up the scantily clad waitress who had delivered our drinks, we then got buttonholed as we crept off for our appointment.

'Hey, you chaps are up to something and I insist on coming along too.'

As the doggedness of an addict is hard to deter, I resorted to gentle persuasion.

'Listen, Tony, we are having lunch with our boss and some exceedingly boring American clients but, as we are early, you are welcome to join us for just one drink in the bar first.'

This concession was to prove a great mistake. Following a lively spat with the barman over our intruder's pungent smoking material, Rupert arrived ten minutes early.

'Hullo boys; mine's a Negroni, I can't stand that vampire brew. And who might you be, sir?'

I could tell, by the electric smile which did not touch his eyes, that our leader was not impressed by the lime green linen suit. He became far less so as his hand was clasped in a clammy palm and he was loudly hailed in plummy, mid-Atlantic tones.

'Tony Cornell is the name, captive insurance is the game. You must be the guv. I saw you alighting from your wheels in the square yesterday; wonderful repro job.'

The acerbic reply contained more venom than a rattlesnake. 'Just to put you straight, as you are obviously a car buff, the automobile happens to be an original 1951 Bentley Continental. And "Guv" happens to be Rupert Wellington-Green, at your service.'

'Glad to know you Rupe. I was just reminiscing with Nigel over the fun we used to have when I was a broker at Lloyd's with him a few years back.'

Having driven a few more nails into the coffin that my career was rapidly becoming, Tony disappeared to the loo, probably to finish off his spliff in peace.

'Where on earth did you dig up that ghastly grasshopper? I have rarely encountered a more vulgar person. People who cannot behave when they are drinking should be banned from consuming alcohol altogether. I don't care how you do it but get rid of him.'

'Right, sir. I will tackle this immediately. Excuse me.'

I left Chris to placate a steaming Rupert whilst I went off to locate my embarrassment in the adjacent facilities. Only one of the leather-covered, brass-bound stall doors was closed so I took a chance and rapped on it.

'Tony, are you in there?'

'Just little old me. Who were you expecting, Superman? If you are alone, I will come out.'

As the bolt was drawn, the door swung open to reveal my un-wanted guest perspiring profusely and clutching a rolled-up 50 franc note.

His bleary eyes regarded me intently. 'Bingo. You want some?'

I was rapidly becoming exasperated. 'No I do not. Listen, Tony, I will be blunt. Not only are you unwelcome, but also you are seriously pissing off the source of my very lucrative meal ticket. When we leave here, please just wave pleasantly and get lost.'

146

'Great, Nigel. So I am not good enough for you any more, eh? You have a conveniently short memory. Anyway, I don't want to be where I am not wanted so I shall bugger off and you can go and f*** yourself.'

'My chief will do that for me if you do not disappear soon, but thanks for getting lost. I will look you up later in the week.'

When we emerged from the rest room, the whole game plan changed due to the arrival of Lee and his very inebriated wife.

'Nigel! Remember your fiery Aunty Bridie? It's time for blast-off!'

As she staggered towards me across the bar area with scant regard for the furnishings, Chris, Rupert and husband Lee observed her erratic progress in silent horror. I immediately made the absurd mistake that people so often do when dealing with important over-imbibers. I behaved with exaggerated charm as if nothing was amiss and, grabbing a fluttering hand, I pressed it to my lips.

'Bridget, what a true delight it is to be in your sunkissed presence once again. Let me feast my eyes upon you for a moment.'

Although some years my senior, in spite of excessive self-abuse, Mrs Derbyshire still retained a firm, athletic body and not too many wrinkles had invaded her visage. Also, her expertly coiffeured shock of flame red locks, though a trifle ruffled, seemed to be weathering her behaviour admirably.

She regarded me with disdain. 'Come on, you can do better than that. Give me a proper hug, not some faggy, Froggy hand peck!'

As she threw her arms around me, Cornell, who was lolling against a door jamb behind me smoking a normal cigarette, came into the range of her myopic vision.

'Now what is this? Does it just stand there belching out fumes like a green incinerator stack or can it speak?'

It spoke all right; within minutes Bridget and Tony had bonded and withdrawn to an alcove, locked in addled conversation as they appeared to be rapidly falling in lust.

As this was indubitably Lee's problem, I returned to the bar where Rupert was doing his best to appease stubby hubby as he murmured empty threats. Lee then suddenly squared his jaw with its twin chins and, having pulled himself up to his full 5 foot 9 inches, with crew cut, gave each of us a piercing, manly stare.

'You know something, guys? We only got in from LA last Friday and I have had a lousy time ever since. If that loaded bitch wants to make a damn fool of herself, frankly my dears, I don't give a damn. I now intend to have a ball for the rest of the week so let's start with a proper boys' get-together.'

Lunch on the pleasantly breezy terrace was a great success, much embellished by Chris's humorous repartee which cheered up our guest no end. When we eventually repaired to the bar for *café cognac* there was no sign of Tony or Bridget which, I was delighted to observe, did not appear to faze her husband in the slightest.

As Rupert withdrew to perform his bedside duties, I drove the three of us to our tented encampment at the Beach Club. On our arrival, we were greeted by a bevy of other hard-working delegates which included the tenacious Dr Yu and an infinitely more relaxed Leone Marco.

Following some chaotic volleyball games, I left Chris to take over as entertainments officer whilst I settled down on a sunbed to catch up on my sleep. Little was I to know that this was to be my last uninterrupted slumber for 48 hours.

It was early evening before my idleness was rewarded by having a bucket of iced water tipped over me by the boss on his return to the fold. My rude awakening delighted Lee, whose flowered shorts looked even more like the Hanging Gardens of Babylon as his sagging belly quivered with mirth. Then, as waiters were dispatched to bring more drinks and some nibbles, we were hailed from the water's edge.

'Ahoy there! Request permission to come ashore.'

Rupert frowned at the intrusion and then groaned. 'Oh Christ; just look what the tide washed up.'

One of the most detested directors in our organisation had beached a small launch and was making his way up the beach towards us. Hilly – or Captain Hillingdon to lesser mortals – was a lumbering, slack-jawed buffoon whose considerable influence grossly exceeded his ability. He derived his power through nepotism where, following an unremarkable Army career, he had taken over father's insurance broking firm. When it became obvious that his inept management was destroying the business, the family had persuaded Cousin Rupert to take over what was left of the company. In view of the fact that many worms in the woodwork had been deceitfully concealed before the sale, Rupert had never forgiven Hilly and treated him accordingly.

As the Captain had now upstaged the British contingent by arriving at the conference in his fully crewed Moody 44 yacht, it was time for some bullying, and my chief was in the mood.

'Well, Hilly, I love the nautical garb with the peaked hat. I suppose that now makes you a naval captain which is equivalent to an Army colonel: much better!

'Really, Cousin, that is no way to greet a member of the family. And why are you entertaining a chap who is wearing pansy shorts? He must be either queer, a Yankee or both.'

Lee was not going to take this obtuse comment lying down. 'I am a Yankee, you arsehole. Lee Derbyshire. We met twice before and you really ought to remember the clients who pay your undeserved salary.'

With Hilly now all aback, it was the ex-gunnery officer's turn to fire another salvo.

'Identity really is not your strong point, is it, Hilly? No career Army officer in his right mind who got stuck at the rank of captain, would dream of advertising it. I was a lieutenant-colonel in Burma at twenty-two years old.'

The remark was slightly unfair as this would have been a temporary war promotion when Rupert was probably no more than a substantive lieutenant. However, it was sufficient to infuriate Hillingdon who stormed off in a huge huff with the boss chuckling gloatingly as his victim's glistening bald pate faded into the gloaming.

'He's a randy old goat, though. Leaves his mousy little missus, Mildred, on the boat for much of the trip whilst he goes gallivanting with half the slappers in town. The stupid woman believes that he's attending business meetings.'

On noticing that a rather crestfallen Rolf Farstud had joined the party whilst I had been in 'noddy land', I drew Chris to one side.

'What the hell is the matter with Rolf? He looks as if he has swallowed half-a-crown and coughed up sixpence.'

My friend let out the nasal 'gurk' of suppressed mirth. 'Well, don't laugh, but you remember that somewhat dusky, elfin creature that he was trying to conceal in his beach tent when we passed by yesterday?'

'Vaguely; but I really wasn't paying much attention following the pool disaster,' I replied.

'Well, the naughty old troll had taken her on as a bed warmer for the week but she decided to vary her role and became a wallet cleaner instead. All gone: cash, credit cards, travellers cheques and she even nicked his passport. Pollard is subsidising him but I don't think that he is being too generous.'

Rolf's sensitive radar detected us chortling together as we looked his direction.

'OK, enjoy yourselves at my stupid expense, boys, but I am the one who will be having the last laugh. With Rupert off to see his daughter again and Peter en route to visit his aunt in Menton, if you value me as a client, I look to you for entertainment tonight, Nigel.'

Actually, this did not give me a problem because, in his taciturn way, Rolf was quite a good sort. Also, I was ever aware that his depressive side was most probably due to his treatment at the hands of the Gestapo when he got caught as a Bergen resistance runner during the war.

So, as my chief wandered off, probably not just to visit Elsa, I was left with a mini League of Nations: one Rosbif, one Wop, one Yank, a Frog, a Troll and a Chink in the shape of Dr Yu.

Fortunately, as everyone had a change of clothes in the luxurious club house facilities, we did not have to leave the beach area for dinner. Having consumed mountains of seafood and drunk enough wine to sink a battleship at L'Hamecon de Neptun, everyone eventually agreed that it was time to move on.

Inevitably, at this volatile stage of the evening, opinions on an appropriate nightclub conflicted. The best pick of a sad bunch in Monaco was the Ali Baba, which got my vote for a certain personal reason. Our Paris agent, grubby little Guy, insisted on visiting a more refined bordello in Juan les Pins and was happy to drive us there in his oversized Mercedes. With the state he was in, Leone was the only taker as he probably needed a more sophisticated establishment to cater for his kinky proclivities. The other punters followed my selection.

We were warmly greeted by Madame Vole-Levant, who owned

the Ali Baba and whose overpainted, plump voluptuousness made her the very epitome of a Gallic Madame. Having pressed me to her ample bosom and smeared my cheeks with scarlet lipstick, she conducted the five of us to a large table as two bottles of her best champagne swiftly appeared.

The club was one of those establishments where, as your eyes become accustomed to the gloom, you wish they hadn't. The layout comprised of a dozen or so glass-topped tables complemented by stained velvet upholstered chairs. These were grouped around a tiny, scuffed dance floor where groping couples shuffled to the muted strains of Sacha Distel.

Otherwise, the dive's predominant feature was a small, dimly lit stage on whose boards forgettable cabaret artists performed nightly. The tawdriest regular entertainer was Maurice, an ageing queen who dressed up as Edith Piaf and mimed to scratchy recordings of her songs. After the gigs were over, the little theatre's tatty curtains were always tightly drawn. This provided privacy for acts of a more personal nature, thus enabling patrons to get to know their hostesses better.

Whilst keeping an eye on a hyped-up Dr Yu, who was table-hopping to inspect the club's female wares, I spotted my reason for being there. Sitting at a corner table with another girl and two men, was Monique. On espying her graceful Eurasian form, so totally out of place in such base surroundings, the pangs of my earlier infatu-ation were instantly reawakened. As I had not wished to cheapen my regard for her when we had met the year before by indulging in slap and tickle behind the musty drapes, we had never shared more than a kiss. However, I was now determined to put this right and there was no time like the present.

With all my guests preoccupied, I wandered over to ask Monique for a dance. Unfortunately, I had seriously underestimated the fact that she was not alone. Before I could open my mouth, a menacing looking character got up from her table and barred my way. I am not easily coerced but, when this bald, barrel-chested hulk grabbed my shoulders and grunted in guttural tones, 'She is with me, so beat it,' I did not feel inclined to argue. Therefore, as the toad-like face snarled into mine and pudgy fingers geared for a shove, the pro-

151

prietor's intervention was most welcome.

'Nigel, please come and have that chat you promised me. It has been such a long time and we have so much catching up to do. Sorry to drag him away when you were obviously getting on so well, Carl; have some champagne on the house.'

Madame Vole-Levant led me to her small serving bar and topped up my glass.

'Sorry, my boy, I now remember that you took a big shine to Monique last year and I should have warned you. Your bald friend has acquired her services for the week and part of the deal is that he has to spend some time in here every night.

'I am afraid that Carlo is a very naughty boy. He is a Bulgarian with extensive underworld connections and seems to have money to burn. It is a tragedy that his visit coincided with your conference, but all is not lost. I know that my young lady would love to see you and I am certain that we can work something out.'

With that she patted my hand and left me to get back to my party. By the time I was resettled, Monique had departed with her hoodlum.

Although the incident was somewhat of a disappointment, the gang were having a great time so I joined in the fun and even had a couple of dances. Then, suddenly, serendipity was restored when Madame beckoned me over to her little den.

'There you are, Nigel. Don't ever say that I do nothing for you. Monique just called me.'

With that she pressed a small note into my hand, which I instantly read: 'Tuesday 3 September. 4.30pm. 17, Rue Henry IV.'

I gave my romantic mentor a hug and a big kiss. 'I shall be there in great anticipation and I am ever in your debt.'

Even though it was only 12.30, I was now ready to sling my hook so I arranged for Chris to close the bill before bidding everyone farewell. This was a hilarious exercise as Rolf, Ho Sun and Lee were all enjoying relief on stage and when I said goodnight from under the curtain, they casually waved to me as if they were just watching telly! Having then established the exact location of my forthcoming *liaison d'amour* with the matchmaker, I took my leave and returned to the hotel.

Narrowly avoiding being drawn into a poker game in the foyer lounge with some of my Australian friends, I managed to reach the haven of my room. Some haven that turned out to be.

My slow immersion in a hot bath was barely completed when the telephone rang. I immediately splashed across to the extension over the loo, in the fervent hope that Monique had escaped her monster. My overenthusiastic 'Hullo, is that you?' immediately got me into trouble.

'It's Elsa. Who were you expecting, you callous brute? I have been waiting for you to visit me all day. I am so lonely and have a terrible headache.'

'But Rupert has been with you this evening.'

'I have not seen Daddy since this afternoon. All I want is for you to come and cuddle me, then I know that I will feel better.'

So Rupert had been bullshitting. But, although I felt extremely tempted by this invitation, it was just not worth the risks involved.

'Listen, I would love to visit you but your magnetic attraction might lead me to breach of your stepfather's trust, for which I would never forgive myself. Please settle down and we will see loads of each other tomorrow. Sweet dreams.'

With that, I hung up and climbed back into the bath, only to be instantly disturbed again by a further trilling of the instrument.

'Yes, Elsa!'

The response was preceded by husky laughter. 'You fickle fellow, this happens to be Bernadette. I was just thinking that, as I have not been able to see you since Sunday morning for business reasons, I would offer you all night now.'

Satan's temptations just refused to go away and this harlot with a heart of gold was not even treating me professionally.

'Sorry, Bernadette, I really must get a good night's sleep. I have a mega important meeting tomorrow. Let's take a rain check. Nighty night.'

My posterior had hardly touched the surface of the now tepid water when the phone sounded once again. It was Elsa.

'Right, Nigel, you are going to comfort me whether you want to or not. I am coming to your room now.'

My cold sweat mingled with the moisture from the bath.

153

'Now, Elsa, please don't be ridiculous, of course I want to comfort you, but you could be seen. Marino is just opposite and Rupert's suite is on this floor. I am just off to join a poker game, anyway.'

To my consternation, it became apparent that I was talking to myself and, in the words of the song, 'I had to get out of this place'. Throwing on a robe, I feverishly dialled Bernadette's number.

'I have changed my mind; see you in one second.'

Number 17, Rue Henry IV turned out to be an elegant eighteenth-century mansion built in the French Empire style, which had been converted into apartments. Having grabbed a quick swim off the rocks in the bay below, at 4.15 p.m. I parked the Renault near the front door. I then settled down to wait and see what fate had in store whilst ruminating on my day.

So far, everything had gone off almost too smoothly. Bernadette and I had parted at 8 a.m. to pursue our separate careers, which a cynic might consider were not that dissimilar. Having then returned to my underoccupied room and managed to kip for a couple of hours, I had ordered *café complet* and then phoned Chris whilst performing my ablutions.

As neither of us had heard a peep out of Elsa all morning, we decided on a 'safety in numbers' joint visit to her room which was on his floor. We found the young lady in an uncharacteristically grumpy mood.

'I have thrown my bloody Froggy drugs down the loo. I don't remember going to bed last night and I have only just woken up at ten forty-five,' she complained, as I breathed an inward sigh of relief.

With lots of tender love and care from us boys, by the time we joined Marino for lunch our young Swede was her old self again, if slightly more reserved with me. Somewhat maddeningly, the ageing gigolo had had no problem securing a table at Le Requin Complet, but I did not let this ruffle my feathers. Fortunately, as Elsa was due to visit an old schoolfriend in Antibes after lunch, I was not subjected to niggling questions about my afternoon plans. In fact, everything was looking much rosier during the jolly repast, until presumptuous Pollard plonked himself down at the table, clicking his fingers for service.

'Large Remy, *garçon*. I'm glad I caught you, Nigel. You now have a most important dinner date tonight with Rupert, me and Jean Baleboise. Your presence is also requested, Went, and we are to meet in the Hotel de Paris's main restaurant at seven-thirty p.m. sharp. Don't be late; the Assurance Republique account is most important.'

Although the dinner appointment had seemed only a nominal time constraint, with the hands of my watch crawling towards 4.45 p.m., anxiety started to kick in. To help pass the time, I mused upon the strange circumstances under which Monique had become a Monte Carlo resident.

Her father had been a French Army Officer stationed in Indochina. However, two years after she was born to his native girlfriend, Father got killed at the battle of Dien Bien Phu, the fateful prelude to the West's humiliation at the hands of the Vietcong. Fortunately her father's brother, who held a senior position at Monaco's Royal Palace, was aware of the family secret and provided a home for the mother and daughter in the principality. This was all fine until, 16 years later, Uncle got caught with his fingers in the royal coffers and disappeared without a trace. Thereafter, poor Monique and her mother were obliged to secure their livelihoods as best they could.

At ten to five, these thoughts were disrupted by the chugging clatter of a Deux Chevaux straining its way up the steep gradient to where I was parked. Patience was then rewarded as my date skipped nimbly out of the little contraption with her ample mum waving a cheery salute from behind the wheel. Whilst the Citroen bounced back down the hill in a cloud of dust, Monique ran to embrace me as I emerged from the Renault. She was wearing a cream silken mini dress and matching platform sandals with her dark hair folded back behind her head. Her fine oriental features blushed attractively as she tried to conceal what appeared to be a silver thermos flask under her scarlet wrap.

'What have you got there?' I enquired as we disengaged.

She gave me a dazzling smile. 'It is sustenance. What is in your bag?'

I put on a rueful expression. 'This is only a suit, shirt and tie, as I have suddenly found myself obliged to attend a dinner at seven thirty where swimming shorts and a T-shirt could prove inappropriate.'

'That is probably just as well. Carl will kill me if I get back too late; he thinks that I am shopping with Maman.'

Her pragmatic attitude towards my limited availability did nothing to flatter my ego!

'How on earth could you get involved with that ugly swine?'

'Don't start being silly, now. He is only business and I have to live. I am seeing you because I want to.'

This was fair comment, and I was being silly and wasting valuable time. Before I could kiss her again, she ducked under my arm and, pulling a large iron key from her shoulder bag, opened the large heavy door to the house. Coming out of the bright sunlight, I could barely make out the drab, unfurnished reception area which boasted an uncarpeted marble staircase. Fortunately this was subsidised by an ancient cage-like lift which groaningly hoisted us up to a more brightly appointed second-floor landing. Monique then unlocked a door marked 'D. Cousteau'.

'This is my cousin's apartment, I hope you like it.'

We stepped into a tastefully decorated bed-sitting room dominated by an enormous canopied couche. I watched in mesmerised anticipation as my hostess slipped out of her skimpy dress, beneath which she was devoid of undergarments. She then cruelly restrained my ardour whilst she went to a sideboard and poured two small glasses of dark liquid from her silver container.

'What on earth is this?' I gasped, having gulped down the heady brew.

'Prunelle Erotique,' was the reply, as my attention span evaporated in favour of baser functions.

I shall never know what special ingredient had been added to what I later discovered was sloe gin. However, during that dazzling two-hour window in my life, whenever there was a suggestion of flagging vigour, a shot of the potion acted like rocket fuel!

The fact that all good things come to an end may be a platitude, but there was nothing mundane about the bizarre finale to this idyllic interlude.

I was reclining on Cupid's crumpled crucible, reluctantly about to prepare for my dinner appointment when, preceded by heavy footfalls, the door was violently rattled. Envisaging that this could be a jealous, raging Carl, my first instinct was to inspect the underside of the bed. As this undignified intention was forestalled by my new lover's emergence from the bathroom, I suddenly realised that the intruder appeared to be locking the door's main mortis lock. After establishing this by tugging at the wrought iron handle to no avail, I turned to Monique with all the calm I could muster.

'I don't know what the hell is going on here, but please tell me that you have another key to this door. I really do have to be at the Hotel de Paris to meet my boss and a mega-important client in twenty-five minutes.'

Even though her wide oval eyes conveyed a negative response, she looked so tantalisingly vulnerable standing before me that I was very tempted to take her back to bed. Not quite, though; this whole situation reeked of conspiracy and my prime objective now was escape.

Having wasted five precious minutes frantically going through drawers and cupboards in an unsuccessful quest for a spare key, I began to seriously regret my hedonistic lifestyle. Meanwhile, my new lover, who had made several unanswered phone calls to her mother and cousin, genuinely seemed to be on the verge of nervous breakdown.

'It's all very well for you with your silly dinner party, I shall probably get beaten half to death,' she wailed as she flopped down on a chaise longue with tears now pouring down her cheeks.

Resisting the wicked temptation to say, 'If you can't take the heat, get out of the kitchen', I gave her a reassuring kiss on the forehead. However, at 7.15, it was time for initiative, not sympathy. On opening the shutters of the room's French windows, I discovered an iron veranda hanging over a leg-shattering 30-foot drop to the garden. Fortuitously, slightly to the right and 10 feet below, was a similar balcony, around which an ancient bougainvillea had wound itself. So long as I did not think about it for too long, I had found a way down.

Ignoring my paramour, who was now becoming belligerent, I hurriedly donned my formal garb and performed a feat that I had only read about in children's books. Grabbing two sheets off the bed, I knotted them together and anchored the makeshift rope to a railing. I then precariously descended to the gnarled climber, which proved

strong enough to bear my weight for a final descent to the ground. My suggestion that Monique might emulate my exit route put the lady into an incandescent fury. Thus, as I departed to rescue my career, I was subjected to a formidable barrage of household objects.

The circumstances surrounding our sudden incarceration that evening will ever remain one of many mysteries that I take to my grave. However, just before I returned to London, I did pop in to see Monique's *maman* at their apartment in the Medusa Building. Having received a taciturn welcome, I was relieved to hear that Cousin Cousteau had come to the rescue shortly after my callous withdrawal and the lady's honour had been preserved. The following year, I learned via Madame Vole-Levant that Monique had married Carl and was living in great style with their baby son in a Cap Ferrat chateau. Such is life!

'You are late.'

Nobody could ever accuse Rupert of pulling his punches when he was angry and nothing irritated him more than a tardy person which, at 7.45, I certainly was.

As he had been badly crippled by polio, our dinner guest Jean Baleboise had every excuse to be a cantankerous bore, which he certainly played to the hilt. Nevertheless, even he was taken aback when I was bellowed at in front of the Imperial Restaurant de Paris's elite diners.

'Hold on, Rupert, do not be too hasty. Nigel appears to be a trifle dishevelled and his suit is torn. Maybe there is a reason for his bad manners.'

This somewhat barbed intervention was spoken in perfect English, as Rupert did not even pretend to speak a word of French. Usually, to emphasise his insecure self-importance, Jean would only converse in his native tongue with lesser mortals which, for me, was a con-siderable strain. However, his last remark gave me the opening that I needed.

'Humble apologies, everyone, but actually Monsieur Baleboise has hit the nail on the head. I just had a violent scuffle with a vagrant whilst crossing the gardens outside who tried to steal my wallet. As usual, there was not a gendarme in sight and I wasted a lot of time trying to find one without success.'

Chris Went winced as Pollard smugly stuck his oar in. 'That's very interesting, Nigel. There is a gendarmerie located on the square, not more than one hundred yards from this hotel.'

I had to take what I got from the chief but not from this jerk. 'So what crime have you committed to be so familiar with the local constabulary, I wonder? I am damned if I saw it.'

'OK, that is quite enough,' growled Rupert with a storm warning glinting from his flinty eyes.

This little spat turned out to be the highlight of an excruciatingly dull evening with only brief respite from Ernst Von Staalhein's rowdy party at an adjacent table. During the latter stages of the evening, the Prussian nightmare, who had witnessed my earlier humiliation with glee, decided to run a lobster derby. This was achieved by coaxing live crustaceans with numbers on their shells in lipstick, to crawl across a series of table tops in pursuit of shrimp on strings. A book was then run on the outcome of each race and, before long, half the restaurant's patrons were noisily cheering on their wagers. We were all dying to join in, but Jean's obvious disapproval dispelled such intentions until Chris foolishly lingered too long by the action en route to the loo. Glaring after him, our guest suddenly grabbed his walking sticks.

'Well, I will be off now and leave you gentlemen to compensate for the loss of your Assurance Republique commission via your winnings on the German fish races.'

What a charmer he was! However, we immediately rallied round to appease the twisted little prima donna and all was saved, following a grovelling apology by Chris which temporarily took the heat off me.

Having managed to massage the client's ego for another hour, much to our relief, he thanked us for an enjoyable evening and made to leave. I have to admit that my relief at his departure was not only due to three and a half hours of tedium coming to an end. In truth, the effect of the erotic concoction that Monique had dished out was still very much with me. I was not disappointed when, having seen M. Baleboise off in his limousine, Rupert and Peter wanted some privacy.

After a nightcap with Chris in his room whilst he tried to recontact the girl from the Munich Re, I was on my way to the fifth floor with but one purpose in mind.

Sod's law. In the lift, I ran into Marino who gave me a lecture on the slumbering needs of middle-aged men. Having made a vow of eternal silence and left the ageing Adonis to rest and recharge his fading batteries, I went straight across the corridor to room 514.

When, after five minutes of intermittent pressure, the doorbell raised no sign of life, I gingerly resorted to the small brass door knocker. On my adding a shouted enquiry, the door opposite opened abruptly to reveal Marino resplendent in a white satin robe and fob cap.

'I begged you to give me a break. Why do you hate me so much?'

Following this incongruous utterance, shrieked at the top of his lungs, he slammed his door so violently that I scuttled into to my room before someone blamed me for the disturbance.

Once in my room, having fruitlessly tried 514 on the internal phone network as a final gesture, I sat on the bed knowing precisely where events were leading me. With the selfish irresponsibility of lustful intent, my hand moved towards the telephone, then my fist clenched as the nobler nature within me stirred. How could I betray the trust of a man who was not only my mentor but also treated me like his own son? I agonised with my conscience for all of 30 seconds before picking up the instrument and calling room 327.

After six rings, I was rewarded with a staccato, 'Yes, what is it?'

'Elsa, so sorry my darling, did I wake you? I have just made a decision to stop being a bore. You are absolutely irresistible and I am coming down right now to have a nightcap and cheer you up.'

To my surprise, there was a palpable pause before I got a terse reply.

'Yes, OK. You can't come here though, I will be with you in a minute. I assume that you are still in room 512.'

'I am, but don't you think that …'

She had hung up and the die was cast. I was a little perplexed by her remote tone, though. What had happened to all the billing and cooing? Anyway, this was not the time to worry about that; I had a guest to entertain.

There is a pattern of erotic behaviour which pervades the nubile echelons of Britain's upper crust which is best described as enthusiasm without finesse. It most probably has got a great deal to do with boarding school culture and Roedean had certainly ensured that Elsa was a dedicated member of this 'eager beaver' brigade.

The contrast between the late show and my earlier, more sophisticated matinee was a delight in itself. However, by 6 a.m., my Roman Catholic conscience, on the wings of fatigue and a hangover, was cruelly turning the screw of guilt. Elsa was now fast asleep so, grabbing an orange juice from the fridge, I wandered out onto the balcony and sat in the new day's misty sunrise to review the situation.

The volatile young lady now lying in my bed had been embarrassingly affectionate prior to our consummation, so the prospect of how she might now conduct herself was daunting. What would Rupert do to me if he discovered that I had violated his trust? This did not even bear thinking about, and it was not just the chill morning air that made me shudder as I cursed myself for not exercising more self-restraint.

I tried to take my mind off the situation by focusing on a growing cast of characters on the boulevard below. Were they early risers, late-night revellers, or just vagabonds? I was beginning to realise that this exercise was a pointless diversion when I was hailed from within.

'Darling, what are you doing sitting out there all alone? Please forgive my going to sleep and, if you still love me, you will come back to bed immediately.'

Wincing in memory of my earlier passion-induced declarations, I returned to bed and dissipated my remorse in whirlpool of sensual urgency.

Having eventually called a truce on the pretext of needing the first smoke of my 50-a-day tobacco habit, I concocted a diversionary tactic. Fortunately the company had booked me into a junior suite, so I suddenly looked at my watch in feigned trepidation.

'Good God, Elsa. I totally forgot that I have invited Lee Derbyshire with several other people for a breakfast meeting here at eight fifteen and that is in one hour. Although it will break my heart, you must return to your room immediately.'

'Well, why don't you change it to his room? I will wait for you here, then we can stay in bed all day, or at least until lunchtime.'

'Listen, my sweet, Lee is having severe problems with Bridget over her drunken affair with that shit Cornell, so he is cutting his trip short. Thus, he has insisted that this meeting must be here as, due his domestic imbroglio, his suite is not a suitable environment.'

Elsa pouted, her blue eyes flashing with indignation. 'That's not fair. And it is all because of that pathetic bitch of a piss artist. What does imbroglio mean?'

'An imbroglio is a bloody mess, which is what we have to avoid with your stepfather. If we want to see more of each other like this, we have to be practical. Rupert is always an early bird, whatever he has been up to, and he could easily be popping in to see how you are as we speak. If he gets an inkling about us, I am a dead man and he will probably have your guts for garters too!'

After some tearful protestation, my mendacious ploy worked and, following Elsa's departure, I settled down to catch up on some sleep. This turned out to be about as restful as Richard III's tented night before the Battle of Bosworth and for the same reasons: trepidation and conscience. By 9.30 I was more awake than ever, so after black coffee, a shave and ten minutes under a cold shower, I departed for the Beach Club.

On my arrival, I selfishly woke up an attendant who was sleeping on the shingle like a baby. After he had sorted out one of our tents, I bade him bring me a bottle of Krug and some orange juice. At 10.15 it was a little early in the day, but what the hell, I needed to relax.

Much to my surprise and relief, the next arrival was Chris, the one person I trusted sufficiently to share the burden of my weighty secret. Contrary to his usual bubbling form, he appeared to be in an introspective mood and some nasty welts on his forehead suggested that he had been in a scuffle of some sort.

'Morning, Nige, can I have some of that too?'

I poured him a Buck's Fizz.

'Those are nasty lacerations on your head. What the hell have you been up to?'

'Nige, you would never guess in a million years, so I will tell you.

163

I have been a complete bloody idiot and I need to get it off my chest.'

I was somewhat taken aback by this strange coincidence. 'Well, I didn't exactly cover myself in glory last night, either.'

'You were with your Swiss tart, weren't you? God, but she must have given you a good seeing to, you look totally knackered.'

'Actually, Chris, I failed to make contact as she was away on another mission. Maybe it's time to swap secrets, so let's take our drinks for a little walk along the beach in case someone else turns up.'

When we were a hundred yards, or so, away from the tents, I stopped and turned to my friend. 'OK, you go first.'

Chris looked me in the eye like a dog that has just deposited on the carpet. 'Well, quite simply, I screwed Elsa.'

At this, I was naturally dumbstruck and the conversation briefly lapsed into pantomime repartee.

'You can't have done.'

'But I did.'

'How?'

'In the normal way; I'm no pervert.'

'I don't mean that, you ass. Where?'

'In her room, and the whole event turned into a complete nightmare mystery. Let me tell you about it.'

I gave him a dazed nod.

'As you may remember, Nige, I could not get in touch with my Munich Re friend, Helga, last night. After you had gone off to bonk your gnome from Zurich, I started feeling a bit frisky and, with Elsa only three rooms away, the temptation to pay her a visit was too much. When she answered the door wearing a short, transparent negligee, I cracked straight away and, within seconds, we were down to business. However, as I was getting really stuck in, the bell sounded. Honestly, Nige, I damned nearly shat myself in flagrante as I was sure that it had to be Rupert stopping by. Having disengaged my shrinking manhood and dived to the floor in total panic, there was not a sufficient gap for me to crawl under the bed, to which the scars on my head bear witness. Then, by the time I recovered from my yellow funk, Elsa had disappeared.

'What is so bloody funny?'

I could not help it, this was just too ludicrous for words and all I could do was sit on the beach in fits of uncontrollable laughter.

'That wasn't the door bell, that was me phoning her, you silly bugger. She was with me for the rest of the night. As Bernadette was playing an away match, it opened an opportunity for me to play with fire. We have both behaved like arseholes, though, and, I find your conduct extremely unhygienic!'

My friend joined me in total hilarity.

Strangely enough, these revelations had completely salved my guilty conscience. As my humorous convulsions had drained my final reserves of energy, I declined joining Chris for a swim and sat down on a nearby recliner to finish my drink. I was still savouring my escape from the pangs of regret when a slightly guttural female voice intruded on my thoughts.

'Excuse, please. I am looking for Mr Went who is with the Wellington-Green party.'

I stood up to confront a handsome, full-bodied young lady with platinum blonde hair who was attractively clad in a blue and yellow floral beach sarong.

'You are in exactly the right place. I am Nigel Kemble-Clarkson and that spiky pink blob out to sea is my dear friend, Chris Went. You must be Helga.'

Two green-blue eyes creased up in a mischievous smile. 'I am, indeed, Mr Kemble-Clarkson. Chris phoned me early this morning to invite me for brunch.'

At this point my pal bounded out of the sea like a wet Labrador and took over the proceedings. I was delighted that he had landed his elusive fish at last, as it took him out of an equation which was sufficiently tricky already.

During the next half-hour or so, most of the regular gang arrived at the tented encampment. This included our Churchillian chief plus Elsa who, rather too obviously, failed to make her customary fuss of me.

I was endeavouring to appease Marino for disturbing his rest once more when Rupert called me over to where he was sitting in a deck chair, sipping a Pimm's.

'So, Nigel, you have condescended to join us this morning.'

I sat down in the chair next to him as Elsa looked on nervously.

'That's right, sir, fully back on parade again. Sorry I was late last night.'

Rupert's eyes drilled into me as he growled like a bulldog. 'That was very naughty and don't think for a moment that I fell for your mugging bullshit. You had definitely been up to no good. Then you disappear after dinner and are looking very rough around the edges today.

'You are not usually such a dark horse, so who is she? In fact, I offer you a challenge. I am throwing a small lunch party at Requin Complet tomorrow for old Cyril Barber of the Ocean Assurance. He is very important to us, as you know, and he adores young ladies. I shall bring Elsa, Went is a must with this Rubenesque Hun and I shall expect you to produce your new conquest, who I am sure will be up to scratch.'

Fortunately Elsa had been eavesdropping, which meant that she would accept that I was under pressure to produce a female lunch partner in order to avert suspicion. Some hopes!

I was just beginning to experience a queasy feeling in the pit of my stomach that my special relationship with the boss was under strain, when I got a break.

Peter Pollard was paddling in the light surf when a power boat slowly cruised by close inshore with three topless beauties waving from the sun deck.

'Pierre, Rolf, where is your chunky friend? We are impatient, come and meet us on the jetty by the point.'

Rupert went pale under his suntan. 'Shit, Nigel, we weren't scheduled to see this lot until after lunch. Do you think Elsa has picked up the scent?'

My route back to royal favour was opening up before me, which was to produce an instant juicy bonus.

'I don't think so, shall I get rid of her right now?' I whispered conspiratorially.

'Yes, you can both go and sort out Dr "Who Are You", or whatever his name is, for lunch. He was sitting at the pool bar just now looking rather lonely. Take Went and his new bint with you whilst you are at it. But hurry.'

I got an appreciative pat on the back as I departed on this most welcome mission.

Having immediately extricated a baffled Elsa, along with Chris and Helga, we all headed for the club exit, being careful to make a wide detour around the swimming pool area. As the other two had their own agenda, just Elsa and I were soon driving back to the hotel for a siesta and some room service!

En route, I decided to have some sport in allaying any fears that my young lady might harbour concerning my knowledge of her duplicity.

'So, what did you think of Helga?'

The retroussée nose crinkled. 'She is very sweet in a sort of robust, Teutonic way.'

I sighed philosophically. 'Well, Chris is obviously very smitten. Did you know that he has been desperately trying to contact her since they first met last Monday and only succeeded in doing so late last night,' I lied. 'She most probably arrived to see him at around the same time that we were bonding.'

The combined expression of relief and pique on Elsa's face was a sight to behold.

'I don't know, you men have no morals whatsoever; they hardly knew one another.'

How is it that women are so much better than men at blanking out their own sins of the flesh and taking the moral high ground? Probably because, being virgins at heart, they believe that straying from the path of righteousness is solely down to male corruption.

Elsa stamped her foot loudly, inspiring intolerant mutterings from several Tiptop barflies.

'So, Nigel, I am supposed to sit through lunch with you in the company of some poxy tart? You are obviously doing your best to make a fool of me.'

'How can you look foolish if nobody knows about us? I am going through with this charade to prevent that happening but, if you keep yelling the odds with Rupert due to arrive at any moment, I shan't bother. A lady from an escort service recommended by the Hotel de Paris is most unlikely to be suffering from a venereal taint and has cost a small fortune to organise.'

'Alright, you bastard, I will accept your crap, but if you touch her I will rip her tits off.'

In all fairness, my only 'crap' was an embellishment of Bernadette's job description. However, even though she had been delighted to take on the assignment, professional pride had to be satisfied and there were a couple of caveats involved. Firstly, that she be treated with due respect as my partner, and secondly, that the mission fell into her fee-paying category. To my amazement, Bernadette suggested that the latter requirement could be discharged via my settling the room 514 laundry bill at the end of the week.

'In this way you can put me on your business expenses so long as you don't mind your accountant thinking that you are a very dirty boy,' was Bernadette's justification for her bizarre terms.

Although this smacked of paying your adversary's straw bill following a horse race, I agreed and we were all set.

As Rupert arrived to collect Elsa, Chris and Helga from the Tiptop, I slipped off to pick up my contentious date from the hotel and drive her to our lunch rendezvous.

By the time we arrived, our quintessentially extrovert main guest, Cyril Barber, was already regaling the assembled company with his latest tall stories.

He was splendidly clad in a cream three-piece linen suit embellished with an Albert watch chain plus a red and yellow polka dot bow tie and matching handkerchief. The bristling moustache which punctuated his florid jowls was a tribute to his having attained the rank of Group Captain in the war time RAF without ever becoming airborne. Ever proud of this dubious achievement, he would aver, 'I was too fat to join the fliers but I was awfully good at showing them where to go and then bringing them home afterwards.'

Although Cyril had started his career as a broker, nobody was surprised when, on his father's retirement as marine underwriter of Ocean Assurance, he was appointed to replace him. Nepotism will out!

My ordeal began as I introduced Mademoiselle Bernadette Davos to the assembled company. Whilst Chris and Helga, who were in on the plot, feigned previous acquaintanceship, Rupert seemed impressed and Peter leered his approval. Ho Sun's reaction, however, was quite extraordinary as he writhed bashfully and got as near to blushing as his yellow skin would allow. My escort's indulgent smirk confirmed that the doctor was a member of the room 514 club. Meanwhile, Elsa's childish attempt at haughty condescension was instantly offset by Cyril's booming approval.

'Wonderful to meet you, my dear. I do like women with meat on their bones, and insist that you and Helga sit either side of me at lunch. Incidentally, as I have had my pink gin quota and am quite famished, can we go to the table soon please, Rupert?'

'We are still waiting for the gallant Captain and Mildred. It was you, Cyril, who wanted to include Hillingdon because of his involvement in setting up your Korean agency with Dr Yu.'

'You are quite right, old man, but as he is probably still flogging his crew at the gratings and his absence will hardly cause a social vacuum, let's go ahead without him.'

As we finished our drinks and adjourned to the dining area, I felt mildly irritated that my least-favourite colleague had been invited in the first place. Had I known what disruption he was about to cause, this feeling would have been closer to panic.

Once we were seated at the table, even Elsa perked up as the occasion got off to a jocund start with everyone talking humorous nonsense at the same time. We had just ordered more aperitifs, when the old soldier arrived with his vapid little wife, whose pale skin did not reflect Côte d'Azur yacht life.

'Mea culpa, mea culpa,' he blustered. 'Mortified to be so late, Cyril, Rupert, everyone. Some long-haired, degenerate Froggy rammed his dinghy into my stern and I …'

He had spotted Bernadette and, as he froze, the look of sheer panic on his face was not missed by anyone except his doting little wife.

'That's right, dear; nobody wants to hear about your marine casualty at an insurance party. I don't think that I have met everyone before, though. I do know Elsa, but who are these two pretty young things?'

Fortunately, Mildred had also failed to notice the glare of total disdain with which Bernadette fixed the hapless Hilly, which made the shark jaws adorning the walls look friendly. I never discovered what demands he had inflicted upon this lady in her professional capacity, but they must have been formidable as she was no prude.

You could have heard a pin drop as Rupert introduced courtesan to spouse, who once again innocently relieved the tension.

'Bernadette, what a lovely name; just like the saint. You must be a Catholic like us.'

This ingenuous observation softened the vindictive expression slightly.

'You are quite right, Mrs Hillingdon, but I am afraid that my faith has lapsed somewhat. You must be a saint, though, to put up with that devil. Funnily enough, the last time I encountered your husband, I could have sworn that his name was Major Hawthorn.'

At this point, the rest of us were holding our breath.

'Oh, how lovely that you two have met before. It must have been at a regimental do, as you are confusing Hilly with his best friend, Binky Hawthorn. We must get you off to confession really soon.'

As I narrowly averted firing a Campari Soda down my nose, Helga waded in for her introduction and, amazingly, everything more or less settled down. Although the dramatic interlude had put a temporary dampener on events, some excellent wine swiftly restored bonhomie.

Unfortunately, the hurdle that I had just managed to scrape over was only the first. The second appeared just after the main course, in the form of an obviously coked-up Tony Cornell. This obstacle was going to be more of a water jump as the roué crashed against our table, waving his bandaged right hand in everyone's face.

'I thought that this must be the toff's table until I spotted a slapper batting out of her league. She's with my erstwhile London boozing mate, I'll be bound. Well, Nigel, I hope that you have got some spare cash to cover the legal costs when I prosecute her for breaking my hand in her door.'

As host, it was incumbent upon Rupert to rescue the situation and he played a blinder.

'Listen, you odious little swine, I loathed you when we first met and if you do not remove yourself from this restaurant instantly, I shall take great pleasure in personally evicting you. Fortunately, as you are incapacitated, I shall only have to soil my left hand when I give you a good thrashing. Do not dare to speak another word.'

As my tormentor departed, muttering dire threats, I managed to promote a round of jeering applause which was enthusiastically taken up at other tables. Four faults, saved again; but only just.

Even though Elsa was far more relaxed with my escort's presence, as her professional status became evident, I was getting some exasperated glares from Rupert and Peter was purring. Meanwhile, Mildred had withdrawn into a brooding silence, which could have been due to her husband's increasingly inebriated state.

Anyway, the party was soon back in full swing and it was not until the cheese was being served that we were interrupted once more. The interloper this time was a smartly dressed, swarthy gentleman who removed his red fez as he addressed the boss.

I am Captain Genklik, Agent of the Turkish Government Fleet, and you must be the esteemed Mr Wellington-Green.'

Rupert stood up and shook the proffered, well-manicured hand. 'That is so and I am delighted to meet you. To what do I owe the pleasure of your company?'

Perfect white teeth flashed from the handsome countenance in Bernadette's direction. 'I was wondering if I might crave your indulgence whilst I have a private word with your guest and my old friend, Mademoiselle Davos?'

'My dear chap, of course you may; that is, if her luncheon partner, Mr Kemble-Clarkson, has no objection.'

With the wheel of fortune turning in my favour again, resistance was out of the question and the two of them adjourned to the bar area with my blessing.

As soon as they were out of earshot, Rupert beamed around the table jubilantly. 'What a break. That chap is the key to a prime piece of business that we have so far failed to secure because of local politics. I will try to lure him into the party on their return, but please try to play down the booze as he is most probably a Muslim.'

Cyril banged the table. 'I am right with you Rupert. I too would love to get my hands on that account and I am very happy to work with you.'

Mrs Hillingdon grabbed her moment. 'Well, I think that my husband and I should be getting back to the boat. He does not seem to be quite himself at the moment and we would hate to jeopardise your Islamic venture.

'Also, Cedric, I am somewhat confused over your past association with that girl. I would hate to think that you might feature in her very long confession!'

As Hilly was led away like a naughty schoolboy, the use of his detested first name by Mildred indicating her fury, Dr Yu rose unsteadily to his feet.

'Why is it that important gentleman choose to wear red lampshade on head? Very strange.'

Our laughter was just subsiding when Captain Genklik returned with Bernadette, who approached Rupert.

'Abdul would love to stay for coffee, if that's all right Mr Wellington-Green, then he has to fly.'

After half an hour, we all bade a fond farewell to our charming temporary guest. Business cards had been exchanged during a most convivial sojourn and a date had been fixed for lunch in our boardroom during his imminent visit to London.

All of a sudden everything was coming up roses for me, in spite of the fact that 20 minutes later, Bernadette took her leave.

'Mr Wellington-Green, Mr Barber and all of you, I very much regret that I have to depart now as I am due to take tea with my aunt. It really has been a most illuminating occasion, for which, many thanks.'

Whilst escorting her to the taxi rank, I stopped in the porch.

'It's that fellow Abdul, isn't it, you naughty girl?'

'Maybe,' she responded coquettishly.

I kissed her cheek. 'Tell me, what are the Turks like in the sack?'

Forgetting her veneered image for a moment, she turned to me with a twinkle in her eye. 'They f*** like they drive: reckless abandon with a tendency to ignore No Entry signs.' With that, she departed.

When I returned to the table, everybody was in great form, especially Cyril, who appeared to have just spilt his port whilst arm-wrestling with Rupert. As I sat down, he gave me a brief round of applause.

'Superb, Nigel. Trust you to spice things up. She was a hooker, wasn't she? Do not answer that. I can honestly say that this has been the most unusual and certainly one of the most enjoyable luncheons that I have ever attended. I do not want it to end and I am sure that, with a bill clocking up like the National Debt, nobody will object if Nigel leads us in one of his famous rugby singsongs.'

The management did successfully intervene after a third rendition but this did not prevent the party continuing until 9.30. Hardly an all-time record, but not bad for a business lunch.

Whilst I was waiting for a valet to deliver my car, Rupert beckoned me to one side with a serious look on his face.

'Nigel, I am too sozzled now, but I think it is high time that you and I had a one-to-one chat. How about a livener at the Café de Paris at eleven a.m. tomorrow?'

I readily agreed, and was far too merry to be anxious over this request until I awoke feeling like the wrath of God the following morning. By the time I arrived at the hallowed venue my concern had dissolved into melancholy resignation. However, to my great relief, when the boss arrived couple of minutes later, he was looking remarkably chipper.

Having given me one of his bear hugs, which was always a good sign, and secured a couple of Bloody Marys, our somewhat bleary eyes met.

'I am most concerned about Elsa.'

My heart almost collided with its spicy starter on its way to my mouth!

'She really has not been herself since that crack on the head. I am sure that you noticed how subdued she was for much of the lunch yesterday.'

A warm infusion of relief seeped through my veins. 'Well, that was probably because you allowed her to drink so little alcohol. A tall order, considering the company she was in, sir.'

'That's as maybe, but I have booked both of us on a flight home this afternoon. You and Peter will have to organise things as you see fit for a couple of days and I would like to say that I am delighted with your performance at the conference to date.

'Buster is going to be the winner here. He will have the time of his life rogering his way home in the Bentley. Most Frogs will never spot the difference between a chauffeur and a British gent!'

On bidding farewell to the two of them later in the day, I did experience a small lump of regret in my throat. However, I managed to console my sense of loss with the thought that I still had a laundry bill to justify, and Helga was bound to have a friend.

After all, that is what insurance is all about!

9

An American Dream

Looking back over the years I still cannot believe how my accidental career in boring old insurance turned out to be such a delight. Not only did the job provide for a very reasonable standard of living, but also it enabled me to socialise and travel the world in luxury at minimal personal cost.

Of all the countries that I visited, my great favourite was the USA, where I also carried out two most enjoyable residential missions. It has to be admitted, however, that my fondness for our transatlantic cousins was strongly influenced by the favourable attitude of the American female towards the British male.

Undoubtedly this has something to do with our diction which, being reminiscent of 'midnight movie' heroes and villains such as David Niven and Basil Rathbone, seems to act as a nostalgic lure. Thus, whilst playing Stateside, I always ensured that a targeted lady was well within earshot. This usually created a situation where the sound of my British accent instigated contact via her feigned curiosity concerning my origins.

This strategy could falter, however, with ladies of Irish extraction as their presence in America was often due to British abuse of their forebears. Thus, one was liable to be branded as being lower than an American WASP (white Anglo-Saxon Protestant). My contingent plan in such circumstances would be to play my Roman Catholic card. This was particularly effective when I fielded the fact that, in 1679, one of my ancestors had been executed for the faith in Hereford. By using this tactic I developed a long-standing network of Irish American friends; especially in New York.

Unfortunately, though, whilst romantic interludes eased the burden of being away from home, the venereal tide that was sweeping across the world by the late 1970s had to be taken seriously. Therefore, as a precaution against the wrath of God, I decided to form more consistent dalliances in the cities that I visited. In hindsight, this was a naive course, as when I was out of town I am certain that my local 'steadies' were not just sitting around longing for my next visit.

In addition, there was a distinct danger that regular calls might be construed as commitment. I was horrified when Mary O'Connor, from Manhattan, turned up at my office whilst she was in London. Having then discovered, via my ever-disapproving receptionist, that I was in Norway on business, she arrived unannounced at my Oslo hotel and wrecked my weekend skiing plans with a local playmate.

This Scandinavian hiccup finally forced me to review the situation and I decided it was time to stop pushing my luck. In future, relationships whilst travelling would preferably be on a 'coals to Newcastle' basis.

Having instigated my new policy by inviting Pandora, a bouncy young Chelsea socialite, on a forthcoming USA tour, I was highly irritated when a complication occurred. This was due to my corpulent underwriting friend, Ronald Pool, insisting that Phil, one of his budding deputies, should accompany me in order to gain experience. As Ronald's support was vital to many of my enterprises and he had offered to foot all expenses, this was an offer that I could not afford to refuse.

Roughly a decade younger than my 43 years, Phil was an affable, handsome fellow whose company I had already enjoyed on outings with his boss. Therefore, although he was an unplanned encumbrance, his presence on the venture did not pose a real problem: or so I thought!

When we met up at Heathrow on the day of departure, my young guest was not remotely fazed by the svelte 'extra baggage', with whom he was soon getting on royally. One of the qualities I most admired about Pandora was that, in spite of her rather haughty good looks and lofty stature, she had the ability to charm people of all backgrounds. However, obliging Phil to play gooseberry was to pave the way for some of the bizarre situations which occurred later. As he was far less worldly than I had originally assumed, leaving him to his own devices in a country brimming with temptation was asking for trouble. A factor he was to starkly display on our first night in the Big Apple.

Having checked into the Plaza Hotel on 5th Avenue and enjoyed a delicious early dinner, we had just adjourned to the Oak Bar for a brandy, when Phil suddenly disappeared. Assuming that he had opted for an early night, Pandora and I relaxed over a couple of drinks and then decided to follow his example.

Much later on, I was rudely awakened by the grating burr of my bedside telephone. Noting with irritation that it was 3.35 a.m., I grabbed the instrument before it disturbed my deep sleeping partner and growled a clipped 'Yes'. On the line was an obviously highly agitated Phil, who begged me to join him immediately. The intense urgency of his tone defied objection so, slippered and gowned, I made my way to his room down the corridor.

On entering through the open door, I found Phil slumped in a chair, still fully clothed and shaking like a leaf. His hair and attire were dishevelled whilst his shoes and lower trousers were wet and covered in mud. Before I could think of something suitable to say he turned to me with a baleful look on his face, his eyes brimming with tears

'Nigel, you would not believe what a dreadful night I have had. Terrible, terrible'.

Pouring us both a Jack Daniels from the minibar, I decided on the tough approach and told him to stop acting like a wimp and explain himself properly. What unfolded was a horror story too crass to interrupt.

'After dinner, I thought I would give you and Pandora some time alone together, so I decided to go for a walk. Just as I was leaving the hotel, I bumped into this stunning black girl who asked me to buy her a drink. We then popped into a piano bar up the road with lots of baseball bats, gloves and photos on the walls,'

'Mickey Mantle's,' I prompted.

'Probably. Anyway, Boula was incredibly friendly and after we had shared a bottle of wine, she asked me if I would like to take her home. This seemed like a good idea at the time, particularly as I have never been out with a coloured lady before, so we grabbed a cab to her place which was at the other end of the large park opposite.'

177

At this, I involuntarily choked on my drink, and did 'the nose trick' down the front of my dressing gown, which stopped Phil in his tracks.

'No, please go on,' I croaked. 'This can't possibly get worse.'

'OK, if you are all right, Nigel, I will. Quite frankly, the girl's flat turned out to be a real shit hole. Having climbed up some rickety iron stairs, she let me into a dingy, rather smelly bedsit with nasty brown stuff running down the walls. Hardly a romantic setting but, remembering your stolid philosophy, I decided to think of England and maintain the aim of the mission, regardless.'

I made a mental note to be more circumspect when giving frivolous advice to impressionable youngsters. The horror story continued.

'So, having been given a tumbler of vodka and Coke, I decided to get down to some snogging on the only bed's unpleasantly stained counterpane. I had barely got off first base when the door burst open and two bloody great Rastas burst in and accused me of violating their sister. Honestly, Nigel, they were evil-looking bastards. I damned nearly shat myself when, after some extremely vicious remarks, one of them pulled out a flick knife and said: OK, so let us see your money, honky.'

Seeming somewhat more relaxed as he got into the alcohol lubricated flow of his story, Phil lent forward and gripped my arm. 'In desperation, I whipped out my wallet and hurled it between the two bruisers where it hit the wall in an explosion of credit cards and dollar bills. Whilst they were distracted, I shoved Boula into their path and made it out through the door. I swear I got down that crappy stairway on the hand rails without touching a step.'

Fortunately, Phil kept himself in remarkably good physical shape, which is probably what saved him from a potentially lethal situation.

It transpired that our young hero's ill-wishers had clattered after him screaming like banshees which recruited numerous other un-friendly dark-skinned gentlemen to join the hue and cry. The fugitive had then fled through a concrete jungle, pursued like Dickens's Oliver when he had been hounded along the Strand.

'I swear to you, Nigel, these guys really wanted blood and, with my breath and adrenalin seriously flagging, thank God I found myself amongst some trees. Then, when the undergrowth became dense, I dived into it and lost the bastards.'

I had noticed that, in addition to the state of his lower regions, Phil's jacket was torn in several places.

'That was a nice suit,' I unkindly observed. 'But how did you manage to get back to the hotel?'

In a far more confident tone, I was told, 'Piece of cake. I picked up a cabby on one of the roads that cuts through the green. He moaned like hell when I told him all my money had been pinched, but the hotel coughed up.'

As the young man was now verging on bragging, it was time to bring him down to earth. 'So how much money did you manage to donate to the Black Power benevolent fund?' I enquired tersely.

'Eh, about a hundred dollars, I think.'

I laughed. 'Do me a favour, Phil. I can see by your face that you are lying through your teeth. How much?'

He looked at the floor and mumbled, 'Six hundred dollars, or so.'

I was taken aback. 'Christ Almighty, that's about all your tight boss gave you for the entire trip. If he finds out about this fiasco, he will not forgive either of us: you for behaving like a complete tosser and me for letting you do so. Don't you read the papers? Everyone knows that a well-dressed white person who goes anywhere near Harlem, even in the daytime, might as well jump off the Empire State Building.'

My short tirade over, I suddenly felt sympathy for Phil's crestfallen demeanour. 'Anyway, I will cover the cash but you can bloody well sort out your credit cards, then buy yourself a new suit.'

Obviously relieved at my generosity, Phil got cocky again. 'Actually, I have sufficient decent suiting with me, thank you Nigel.'

I decided that it was time to return to bed before I lost my patience.

'Please do me one favour, Phil. Don't be a prat all your life, take a holiday; even if it's only for this trip.'

My request was not heeded.

The rest of our time in New York went reasonably smoothly and Phil certainly did his stuff on the client front, barring one exception.

Grant Wilson owned a local broking company and put a great deal of business my way. He was a wonderful, larger-than-life character who entertained lavishly; which probably accounted for his 250-pound frame. Unfortunately, his third wife Beth Anne, who was at least 20 years his junior, tended to be anybody's after a couple of drinks, which was all too frequently. Although Grant appeared to tolerate her struggle with fidelity, I knew that he did not take kindly to men who took advantage of it.

Not surprisingly, when the Wilsons took us to dinner at the exclusive Crystal Room in Central Park, Beth Anne was all over Phil like a rash. Much to her credit, Pandora did a stalwart job in trying to sabotage the flirtation with an avalanche of vapid small-talk. However, by the end of the meal both Phil's resistance and Grant's *joie de vivre* were fading fast.

Fortunately the deteriorating situation was halted when we went on to Regines, a trendy nightclub, where Pandora ran into Emily, an old schoolfriend. The statuesque, zany brunette was obviously trawling for someone to subsidise her East Side apartment and, after a briefing from her old dormitory mate, Phil did not stand a chance. Thus, much to Grant's satisfaction, Beth Anne's chagrin and my extreme relief, we departed at 3 a.m., leaving the new lovebirds welding their bodies together on the dance floor.

Inevitably, a New Orleans stopover always just happened to coincide with a weekend in the itinerary of my American business trips. The simple reason for this was that, barring the often muggy weather, this unique city was always a total joy to visit. Much of its fascination centred on the colourful ambience of the ancient French Quarter which contained a myriad of jazz parlours, gourmet restaurants and risqué nightspots. However, the icing on the cake was the friendly, relaxed and humorous quality of the people who worked and played in this quaintly decadent environment.

We flew in from New York late on Friday evening and checked into the Quarter's finest hotel, the Royal Orleans, all set for a traditional brunch at Brennans on the following forenoon. With its red-bricked cloisters and lush courtyards bursting with tropical flora, this world-famous restaurant managed to do more to eggs than the most depraved cockerel could conceive in his wildest dreams! As we sipped our Irish coffees the following afternoon, after a superlative leisurely repast, I produced a hotel map of the city and passed it to Phil.

'I don't want to be a bore but, remembering your wee setback in New York, I thought that this might be of use. The areas that I have shaded in represent extreme danger. We love you, so please avoid them.'

He studied my handiwork.

'You have quarantined two-thirds of the town.'

'Exactly,' I emphasised, 'but there are still plenty of places where you can enjoy yourself and I will point you in the right direction.'

At this time the naughtier venues in the city – many of which were sadly destined to be suppressed for the 1985 World Fair and never re-opened – still thrived. Pride of place on Bourbon Street was Lucky Pierre's. Here, in the ornate bars and salons, a legion of young ladies from the local seminaries could be found who were financing their degree courses via the world's oldest profession. The nice thing was that one's encounters in this establishment were dignified by the fact that the noble cause of education was being served.

It was here that I sent Phil on Saturday evening to satiate his needs while Pandora and I were entertained by Bernie Clancy, who had no involvement with Ronald's organisation.

Bernie's intake of booze would have labelled him an alcoholic anywhere other than in New Orleans. After treating us to an excessive dinner at Antoine's, he insisted that we adjourn to the nearby famous singles bar, Pat O'Brian's, where we were joined by his girlfriend, Rita. This bawdy vamp, resplendent in a bejewelled white cowboy outfit complete with boots and hat, was apparently a leading light in the State Legislature.

Having bribed ourselves onto a table in the packed garden area, we ordered some Hurricanes, the bar's secret formula cocktail. This brew was so volatile that the establishment's insurers insisted on reserve stocks being stored out of town in view of the fire hazard: not just to the bar but to the French Quarter!

As we settled into the swing of things, with posh Pandora dealing with the vulgar fray splendidly, who should come staggering towards us but Phil. He was sporting the hostelry's logoed football cap at a jaunty angle whilst endeavouring to manoeuvre an equally inebriated, similarly behatted, redhead through the throng.

'Hi Nigel, hi everyone; meet Delores. We fell in love half an hour ago. Isn't she glorious?'

'Glorious Delorious,' the new date yelled as she dropped her Hurricane and plonked herself on top of our table. Then, lifting her T-shirt, she flashed an ample pair of breasts at everyone.

Rita found this incredibly funny and fell off her seat laughing.

As Pandora and Bernie tried to restore some form of order and secure another round of drinks, I pulled Phil to one side.

'What about Lucky Pierre's? Didn't you score?'

He eyed me with the wide-eyed intensity of a drunk. 'Bloody great. Nineteen-year-old dish studying at Tulane University.'

'Well, where is she?' I enquired.

Phil put on a devastated expression. 'Had to let her go. F***ing meter running too fast. I even got charged for feeding her in our hotel grill afterwards. Lots of God-given talents, though. She was a bleeding divinity student of all things!'

'That's New Orleans for you,' I shouted, as we collapsed into each other's arms in fits of mirth.

When we had recovered, Phil chortled, 'I think that I need a lie down with Delores to recuperate.'

I gripped his arm. 'Remember your map. I do not want you ending up in the Mississippi.'

He tapped his nose and winked. 'Once bitten, twice shy. Don't worry about a thing, Nigel.'

Phil and 'glorious Delorious' then wended their unsteady way into the mayhem that was Bourbon Street on a Saturday night. The rest of us, having had our photos taken as we sang 'Dixie' with some gargantuan basketball professionals, proceeded to O'Flaherty's for the inevitable nightcap. In our state, this was not a wise move.

Unlike the Dublin taverns that I frequented with my dear, now late, friend, Liam Galligan, the proprietors of this 'colonial' version took themselves far too seriously. Instead of the usual raucous community singalongs, during the O'Flaherty brothers' renderings of Republican dirges, silent adulation from patrons was mandatory. To enforce this antisocial code, stalwart bailiffs were on hand and it was not long after our arrival that we attracted attention from this quarter. Rita's tuneless screeching of the 'Tied up in a black velvet band' chorus sentenced her to phase one discipline: a piece of sticking plaster stuck over the mouth. Bernie immediately let rip a string of obscenities at the perpetrator which moved us swiftly on to phase two. We were all evicted and escorted across the road to another bar which, surprise surprise, just happened to belong to the O'Flaherty family.

Frankly, it has always amazed me that patrons were prepared to put up with all this crap and still go back for more. The old New Orleans syndrome again, I suppose.

Enough was enough for one night, so after lots of hugs and kisses, farewells were bid and we went our separate ways. Following removal of the punitive plaster which erased her bright red cupid bow lips, Rita went on her way with a large white rectangle across her make-up. This ridiculous spectacle had Pandora and me giggling all the way back to the hotel.

Unfortunately, the boss of the largest local shipping line, who was one of my top clients, was not in town the following week so we were obliged to have dinner with him on Sunday night. Therefore, following a long lie-in next morning, I boringly suggested to Pandora that we should try to have a moderate day in order to recharge our batteries. Unfortunately, I was unable to transmit this game plan to Phil as there was zero response from his room.

Having offered up a silent prayer that our companion's supine behaviour was solely due to him sleeping it off, we left the hotel en route for the Acme Oyster Bar on Canal Street. Apart from oysters, the incredibly tasty variety of fish dishes that this steamy venue concocted ensured consistent patronage without the need of an alcohol licence. A wise choice for a recuperative lunch.

As my granny often said, 'The way to hell is paved with good intentions', and as we passed the Old Absinthe Bar, my resolve cracked.

'Pandora, we really should grab a quick drink in here as it is steeped in Napoleonic lore and probably the Quarter's most famous watering hole.'

Ignoring her quizzical expression, I ushered her into the dive's dingy interior where stylish squalor confirmed its historical significance. The rotten panelled walls were adorned with grubby flags, truncated ties and yellowing calling cards whilst various dusty busts and pictures of the little Corsican genius were also displayed.

Having settled down with spicy Bloody Marys, I excused myself to answer a call of nature in the odorous facilities to the rear of an adjoining snug bar. En route, who should I discover in one of the battered wooden alcoves but a patently exhausted Phil. He was sipping champagne with a flashily painted half-cast woman, old enough to be his mother, whilst trying to hide from me behind a menu.

With my lavatorial needs accelerated by the shock, I could only manage a swift 'I don't believe it' as I passed by.

On emerging from the loo, I discovered that Phil, *sans femme*, had joined Pandora in the main bar and was also getting stuck into a Bloody Mary.

I was not amused. 'Does your transience know no bounds or are you trying to set some sort of record? Who the hell was that?'

On receiving no answer, I appealed to an obviously confused Pandora. 'Did you not witness the ratbag that this lecherous young devil was carousing with next door? She really was the ultimate pits.'

Phil suddenly came to life and tried to re-establish his dignity. 'I just love listening to people discussing me as if I were not present.'

I turned on him. 'You won't be bloody present if you go on like this much longer.'

Realising that I was kicking a man when he was down, I moderated my aggression. 'Listen, old boy, what's done is done, but we must all be on the ball when we meet Burt and his heir apparent, Rollo, tonight. I suggest that we now finish our drinks, have a non-liquid lunch and then reinvent ourselves via a siesta.'

Over Acme fried oysters Phil revealed that, halfway through the night, Delores had confessed that she was married to a violently jealous black jazz trumpeter. Furthermore, if she failed to get home before he returned from his cabaret stint in Fat City, near the airport, she risked a severe beating. Apparently her body still bore bruising from the last time she got home late. Naturally, Phil had responded like a gentleman. However, having sent Delores off in a taxi at 3 a.m., he then managed to get himself hooked and landed by the sleazy bint that I had just seen him with.

'I did not visit the "no-go zone" on your map, Nigel,' Phil protested.

'I did not shade in disease-hazard areas,' I retorted, which seemed to put the poor fellow into a morosely pensive mood.

When we returned to the hotel, Pandora decided that she would go shopping so, having sent her on her way with a kiss, I retired to bed for a rest, hoping that my charge was following suit.

As I had displayed a 'Do not disturb' sign, I was extremely irritated at being aroused from a deep sleep an hour or so later by urgent tapping on my door. When I eventually responded, who should be standing in the corridor but a wide-awake Phil. Having restrained myself with difficulty, I quietly addressed him through clenched teeth.

'What the hell do you want and why are you not asleep, as I was before you tried to break down my door?'

'I have to speak to you, Nigel.'

I reluctantly ushered him in.

'You know, Phil, you really are becoming a pain in the arse again. Why are you here?'

What unfolded was pretty unremarkable, except that it seemed to have had a profound effect on the young man's mind.

'Well, Nigel, when I got back to my room, I turned on the telly and there was some form of quasi-religious programme about the wages of sin and all that crap. I was just about to change channels when the theme switched to medical aspects of retribution for lust and fornication. It went on to depict in the most lurid pictorial detail various forms of pox that people can now contract.'

Although this was a subject that I really did not wish to visit, as Phil's intensity appeared to be verging on panic, I deemed it wise to let him purge his soul.

'I thought herpes was a cold sore, I didn't know that you could get it … elsewhere. You should have seen some of the pictures. And it's bloody incurable!'

This was true at the time so, in order to lighten things up a little, I said, 'You seem to be having a prick of conscience.'

Phil thumped the table. 'That's not funny, Nigel!' Then, in a quieter tone, 'Do you think I might have caught anything?'

'Well, you claim that your evil intentions were foiled in Harlem and I would like to believe that Pandora's friend, Emily, was as clean as a whistle. However, you have not been very discerning here, particularly with that moose you were with this morning.'

On receiving a baleful look, I moved on swiftly before getting shouted at again. 'Anyway, I am not a bloody doctor but, by the law of averages, I am sure that you are going to be just fine.'

Phil was obviously not pacified by my vague optimism but, before he could resume his whingeing, he was cut short by Pandora's return.

Plonking down a plastic bag, she stood before us accusingly. 'I thought that you chaps were going to get some rest. Phil, for Christ's sake, sit down before you fall down, I have never seen you look so ghastly.'

'You haven't done much shopping Pandora,' I observed.

'The decent stores are on the other side of Canal Street and I couldn't be fagged to walk that far in this heat, so I just bought some T-shirts plus this as a memento.'

She pulled a large fluted glass out of the bag which was inscribed in green with the Pat O'Brian logo. Admiring the glassware, I chuckled to myself as I knew that the bar awarded these trophies to anyone who drank two large Hurricanes in succession. I would have to keep a closer eye on this lady!

Phil withdrew sullenly and, as it was already five o'clock, there was only time for a brief lie down before preparing ourselves for dinner at the Commander's Palace. This exclusive restaurant occupied two floors of a pillared and stuccoed colonial mansion just outside town, and was the place to be seen if you were 'anyone' in New Orleans.

Having managed to arrive on time, we were warmly greeted by Burt Tolly and his second-in-command, Rollo Benson. I had known these characters for years and, during their steady promotion from ship's officers to executive status, we had shared some memorable times. Both men were highly able and, as Burt was charmingly scruffy and introspective, whilst Rollo was immaculate, bluff and egocentric, they were a perfect blend.

Our hosts entertained us in true Louisiana style but, whilst I kept my end up and Pandora flirted strategically, Phil was a total misery for the entire evening. Amazingly this turned out to be a blessing as, whilst we were all saying goodbye after brandies and cigars, Burt took me to one side.

'Great to meet Phil, and I have to say it is good to know that my main insurer has got someone serious working for him. I have always found Ronald a tad too frivolous and rather suspect so far as his sexual preferences are concerned.'

When we got back to the Royal Orleans, Phil went straight to bed and, over a nightcap in the bar, Pandora asked me why no wives had attended the dinner. I explained to her that this was down to pure Southern chauvinism. The boys had told their spouses that the evening had been a stag affair in order to get a 'pink ticket' and would, by now, be out on the town and up to God knows what.

Fortunately, my bullshit seemed have fobbed off the awkward question as I was anxious to avoid an affront to my lady's fragile sensibilities via her feeling marginalised. However, it was always difficult to read what lay behind those emerald eyes.

In truth, Pandora was right to smell a rat as she had sensed the New Orleans double standard code of conduct, which was similar to Victorian hypocrisy. If a chap was seen beastly drunk with a sailor on one arm and a whore on the other in the French Quarter, a blind eye was turned. However, if one behaved perfectly at a society function but was accompanied by a mistress, a person of darker hue or both, social ostracism would follow. We were well outside the 'blind eye' category. Although the wives would flutter their eyelashes at me when I was alone, they would not condone my presence at a smart dinner party with a woman of obscure identity.

Anyway, getting our most important meeting out of the way early had been most convenient. There was still Houston and Dallas Fort Worth to visit before Friday when I was determined that we would be free to embark upon my special weekend project.

Houston was only an hour away and we landed there late on Wednesday morning having managed to cover most of the important New Orleans clients.

Mainly due to the energy industry, this former rustic Texan enclave was on its way to becoming one of the USA's largest cities. At this time, however, the town was still in its formative years so the commercial area had not sprawled into the vast concrete forest of designer towers that it is today. Fortunately, as I had lived and worked here a few years earlier, many of my business contacts were personal friends. The downside of this was that, when visiting, I was usually invited to participate in field pursuits which Texans love to make both gruelling and dangerous.

Angling from a boat, or even a river bank, always poses the risk of being disfigured or blinded via being struck by a carelessly cast 'torpedo lure'. These hazardous implements are rather like an Ann Summers product festooned with vicious hooks. In spite of the fact that casting patterns are more safely deployed, wade fishing is equally dangerous. Apart from the agonising prospect of stepping on a stingray, one is also exposed to being poisoned via contact with the tentacles of a Portuguese man-of-war or the spines of a catfish. In addition, dragging one's leaky waders through the water, in torrid temperatures and high humidity after a heavy night, is highly likely to cause heart failure.

So far as shooting is concerned – which Americans insist on referring to as 'hunting' – safety considerations are often severely lacking. Admittedly, the pursuit of wildfowl is reasonably well organised, and bringing down the crafty Texan quail certainly requires special skill and patience. However, in the pursuit of deer caution is thrown to the wind to such a degree that it becomes tantamount to braving friendly fire. This has nothing to do with the kill which often involves merely skulking up a tree until sunrise and then blasting the creature at close range with a telescopic Magnum rifle. The real problem is that the average Texan male is a cowboy at heart and often uses a hunting weekend as an excuse to strap on a sidearm. During leisure periods, these are frequently snatched from holsters when pot shots are taken at any tempting target. It is, therefore, most important to make one's whereabouts as obvious as possible at all times. I always wore a bright red Stetson hat which I would justify by saying that it was English hunting pink. Sadly, this did not prevent it being frequently used for target practice; fortunately, only rarely when it was on my head!

The ultimate risk, though, is the 'varmint shoot'. These take place after boozy nocturnal poker games during weekend hunts where they often diverted ugly behaviour from losers who have gambled unwisely. At the sound of a motor horn, all males present pile into the back of open trucks, armed to the teeth and wielding powerful torches. The 'posse' then speeds through the undergrowth, blazing away at armadillos, skunks and any other variety of God's creatures unfortunate enough to get spotted. Although casualties are surprisingly rare, on one occasion I shamefully managed to become one. On taking a pot shot at a bobcat, I put my brow against the metal rifle scope for clearer vision. The gun's recoil gave me a black eye and eight stitches. Rather a pathetic effort for a man trained in firearm skills by Her Majesty's Government. And in front of the Americans too!

Fortunately, as this was an exceptionally brief visit, there was no time to indulge in any sporting pursuits. The most exciting highlight turned out to be spending time with Rush Johnson and his famous partner, Red Adair. At this time, in spite of having already spent a lifetime extinguishing oil rig fires, with the scars to prove it, this ageing pair of stalwarts were still amazingly active.

Sadly, when we met up with them at their downtown office on the evening of our arrival, Red could not stay long as he was due to be in Mexico for an emergency job. He found it hilarious when, during introductions, Pandora walked straight past his 5 foot 3 inches frame and shook hands with a tall staff member who happened to be standing behind him.

'Looking for the Duke, eh?' he laughed. 'I always told him that his worst piece of overacting was exaggerating my height.'

As John Wayne was 6 foot 2 inches, this was true, but otherwise, he had done a superlative job of portraying this intrepid little hero in the film about his incredible life.

Red soon hugged the embarrassment out of Pandora and we all withdrew for drinks in an opulently appointed boardroom overlooking the city's downtown area.

Strangely enough, the two latter-day gladiators were remarkably contrasting human beings. Red, with rusty hair still shining through the grey, was ever a lithe ball of fiery energy. Conversely, the bulbous Rush would lugubriously dispense his ponderous views in a deep Texan drawl that sounded as if he gargled with gravel. Nevertheless, one of the great things they had in common was that they knew how to enjoy their hard-earned money.

A couple of years earlier, I had visited the infamous Miranda nightclub in London's Soho with them. As we entered the main salon, every girl in the place, in total breach of professional courtship rules, had abandoned their temporary beaus. Then, squealing like groupies, they queued up to welcome the duo with kisses and cuddles. Admittedly the boys were waving around sheaves of $100 bills at the time!

Anyway, I allowed this memory to fade as we were served mint juleps by a busty blonde secretary. By this time, Red and Rush had Pandora blushing at their double entendres as they explained a scale model of their latest project, 'Red One'. This was an 'all singing, all dancing', fire-fighting barge which they planned to station in Stavanger to deal with emergencies in the North Sea oil fields.

Although insurers loved this revolutionary concept, it was to fail, as, after much haggling the penny-pinching oil companies refused to bear standby fees. Because this was unworkable, the project was finally aborted which lost Red and Rush a great deal of money. Needless to say, with their inimitable fortitude, they managed to trade through the crisis.

To my consternation, Phil, who had already upset the drinks server by pinching her bottom, started to heckle during our hosts' presentation by asking inane questions. Initially, he had seemed somewhat overawed at meeting these legendary characters, but the relaxed atmosphere, coupled with lethal cocktails, had obviously rendered him devoid of inhibitions. I was, therefore, relieved when Red took his leave, even though he rewarded Pandora with a somewhat over-friendly kiss and promised to organise her a date with John Wayne. Rush then took us on to dinner at the hotel next door.

The slowly revolving Spindletop Restaurant which capped the Hyatt Regency was still something of a novelty, even although much of the view had been masked by new, mirrored skyscrapers. This meant that, if you ate near the windows, you would get intermittent rippling views of yourself which was not always a good thing. As we all settled down at such a table, I discouraged interest in the menu for I knew that our host would not dream of ordering food until we had all downed at least three cocktails.

Whilst Pandora paced herself on Chardonnay and I just managed to keep up with Rush, Phil was starting to lose the plot seriously. By the time we got stuck into some succulent prime ribs with all the trimmings, a surfeit of bourbon and French burgundy had transported him to another planet. Disregarding the rest of us, he ogled and harassed the skimpily attired waitresses, whilst making remarks that would be actionable in today's politically correct climate.

By the time coffee and cognac arrived, it was obvious that Rush had lost patience with Phil's alternately interrupting and then ignoring his rambling stories.

'God dammit, Nigel, this boy's behaving like a one-eyed dog in a meat market,' he growled, giving me an evil, knowing wink.

'I think that we will have to go round the corner and get him fixed up.'

What was being referred to was the Desert Fox, a hostess club situated just behind the hotel where, on occasions in the past, Rush had generously financed my Tex Mex takeaways!

'Will your young lady be upset if we all go on to a cat house?'

Pandora swiftly cut in. 'Only common people are prudish where I come from.'

Rush flashed one of his rare gold-filled smiles. 'Well, I'm as common as shit and I ain't got a prude in me.'

We all laughingly adjourned to go and see what Erwin Rommel was up to.

The nightclub typified the velvet-trimmed, dimly lit, honeytraps that are in abundance around the world for the exploitation of *Homo* non *sapiens*'s baser instincts. In spite of his Sioux girlfriend having recently agreed to become his sixth wife, without reservation (geddit?), Rush was obviously still closely in touch with the establishment. We had barely got through the door when a slinky Oriental number wrapped her half-naked body around him and nibbled his ear. She then showed us to a spacious alcove where champagne was swiftly dispensed as she snuggled up to our purring host.

'Chrissie Sue, meet this fresh faced tenderfoot. His name is Phil, his well is about to blow and he needs someone to cap it.'

Without rising from her seat, the lady made some form of sign, known only to her profession, and out of a small army of ladies from north and south of the Rio Grande, Conchita materialised. She seated her curvaceous brown body close to Phil, who rewarded her with a slobbering kiss that was sadly to prove his sole lecherous achievement of the night. Very soon, with the booze having taken a heavy toll, he struggled off to the loo.

This is where I later found him, sitting on the pan, fast asleep, with his underpants round his ankles, brimming with vomit. Having mopped the lad up as best I could, I decided that it was definitely taxi time. After some half-hearted protestations, we left Rush to enjoy Chrissie Sue, Conchita and whatever other thrills the Desert Fox had in store.

As I had only one client to see in nearby Dallas Fort Worth, we chose to take a late-morning shuttle flight on Thursday.

Although Pandora was doing her best to nurse our errant companion back to health, as he still smelt like a pub carpet at closing time I elected to remain aloof. Had I known that, on that very evening, it was my turn to win the unsuitable conduct award, I would not have been so snotty.

We were visiting Bob Gilbert, who had successfully built up his own marine risk consultancy business. In spite of his irritating devotion to Harvard School of Business dogma, Bob and I had worked successfully together on a number of highly profitable deals. As he loved to party and adored the ladies with the zealousness often found in shorter men, mutual social proclivities probably had a great deal to do with our synergy. I remember this becoming apparent on the first day I met him, some years earlier. We were in the back of a taxi, snarled up in downtown Dallas traffic. It was a particularly humid day and, as we sat there, a beautiful young thing slunk past with her mini-skirted nether regions at head height. Bob turned to me with a wicked glint in his eye.

'You know, Nigel, I would just love to grab hold of that and strap it on like a gas mask!'

The naughty gnome met us at the airport in good time to drop off our baggage at the Fairmont Hotel and drive on for lunch at the nearby Tumbleweed Restaurant. The eatery was one of a national chain where the theme was smart casual, food portions were chunky and cocktails generous. Although the venues were simply furnished, their walls traditionally displayed colourful murals depicting caricatures of local celebrities. In the Texan locations, the waitresses' overfamiliarity often matched their costumes, which comprised of cowboy hat, skimpy top, hot pants and high-heeled boots. We were, therefore, in an ebullient mood by 3 p.m. when Phil and I accompanied Bob back to his office, and Pandora went off in a cab to catch up on the shopping that she had fudged in New Orleans.

Mainly due to our host's pedantry, the afternoon's business agenda took far longer than had been anticipated and it was six o'clock before our meeting ended. As we were all in casual attire, Bob was keen to move straight on to Billy Bob's in Fort Worth.

Before leaving, I phoned Pandora, who was back in the hotel having completed her mission and sounded as if she might have passed by a local version of Pat O'Brian's. She was somewhat miffed at being the only girl at dinner again, so I fell back on the same excuse that I had used in New Orleans. In fact, this time it was true; Bob did fully intend to use his 'pink ticket'. Anyway, my lady seemed appeased but insisted that she had to bathe and get changed before joining us. As this was bound to include all those finger-tapping tasks which delay a good night out, we agreed on a prominent meeting place at nine o'clock.

Fort Worth had been a famous cow town which, in days of yore, was a major marketing terminus at the end of many a gruelling cattle drive. The community had always bred odd characters and, in 1970, a nutty local financier, Bunker Hunt, had attempted to corner the world's silver market.

When this bizarre venture inevitably failed, Bunker and a group of his wealthier friends decided to reinvent the city's entertainment industry. Having acquired a substantial downtown site, where cloven hooves had formally reigned, this crazy band of entrepreneurs constructed the last word in leisure centres and named it Billy Bob's. The vast complex contained no fewer than 42 bars and restaurants, many with cabaret and dancing facilities, plus a large arena for bovine and equestrian activities. It was at a plush lounge overlooking this enclosure that we elected to commence our revelling, and where I had fatefully arranged to meet Pandora.

As imbibing has always has always been a part of my social and commercial life, I can drink whisky, decent wine or beer until the cows come home without losing the plot. However, if I ingest alcoholic beverages to which I am not accustomed, I am likely to become seriously unglued and upset persons of a more sensitive disposition. This was to be the case on that memorable evening in Billy Bob's.

Possibly because I was feeling euphoric in anticipation of the weekend ahead, I unwisely joined Bob and Phil as they experimented in the various ways to concoct tequila-based cocktails. As this involved some swift downing of hot shots, I soon began to feel the effects of my imprudence. Nevertheless, as 'there's nothing exceeds the love of a brother but the wondrous love of one drunk for another', I rode the tide with my new best friends.

Suddenly, our self-indulgent world was interrupted by blaring fanfares from a sombreroed Mexican brass band which had assembled in the bull ring below. This heralded a colourfully adorned detachment of mounted cowgirls and cowboys who rode helter-skelter around the arena. When they had finished firing off their pistols and rifles, their leader, a copiously moustachioed dude, dressed like Buffalo Bill and riding a black stallion, was passed a microphone.

In my hazy state, I just about gathered, via the staccato tannoy announcement, that there was about to be a trick riding and shooting display. This would be followed by the Amateur Night Rodeo Challenge, where members of the audience were invited to ride a bucking bronco or try their hand at cattle cutting. Both challenges were formidable and the second one, based on old branding procedures, involved staying astride a bounding Quarter Horse whilst separating a specific steer from a herd. There was a prize of $1,000 for the winner of each category.

Like the drunks we were rapidly becoming, we stood on our seats to raucously cheer the unremarkable professional displays. Then, when it was the amateurs' turn to try their luck, we jeered as the competitors in the first category were dumped on their backsides by a series of unbroken colts. It was while this was going on that Bob threw down the gauntlet.

'Nigel's a seasoned horseman you know, Phil. Fox hunting, horse racing in Africa, and he even rode some trick ponies on Bill Delgado's ranch outside Houston a couple of years back. How come our hero is not out there showing everyone how it's done?'

After some initial resistance to Bob's chiding, my alcoholically inflated pride got the better of me.

'OK, you bastards, I will have a go at the cutting, but only if you both give me odds of a hundred dollars to ten dollars if I am successful. Also, take that Stetson off your Munchkin head, Bob, and let me wear it so that I am appropriately attired for the venture.'

As I donned my borrowed hat, Phil gripped my arm in concern. 'I will have nothing to do with this Nigel. You must be f***ing crazy.'

'To quote you, Phil: don't worry about a thing. And I will still do it whether you wager Ronald's precious money or not.'

I was actually starting to regret my foolhardy decision, but the die was cast and my addled honour was at stake.

After the last aspiring bronco buster bit the dust, I was first in line to sign the obligatory 'hold harmless' undertaking. This was tantamount to a pre-nuptial agreement with the Grim Reaper, but I was now anxious to get the business over with as soon as possible.

Having got to the head of the queue, I was unceremoniously helped into the saddle of a frisky bay gelding who, worryingly, answered to the name of Bolt. With my head swimming, I desperately clung onto the saddle horn as my mount danced towards a group of milling cattle where the target animal was marked with a splodge of red paint on its head.

Falling off was only a question of when, not if, and rather frighteningly it was not until I was in amongst the herd that my steed decided to dissolve our brief partnership.

God only knows how I did not get seriously trampled. To my eternal gratitude, who should be the first person to come to my aid but Phil. His fitness and agility enabled him to sprint to my rescue before the stewards' assistants could arrive. When they eventually did, it was obvious that Phil's 7th Cavalry gesture was not appreciated as they frogmarched both of us out of the forum to a chorus of catcalls and boos from the crowd.

When Bob then greeted me with, 'Hey, where's my hat?' I could have cheerfully strangled him.

'F***k your hat. I just almost got killed.'

He slapped me on the back in fits of laughter. 'Then my hat is going to get luckier than you tonight. Pandora arrived just in time to witness your downfall and she is mad as hell.'

Bob was certainly not exaggerating. As I limped back into the bar area, covered in sand, muck and blood from a cut on my arm, a seething Pandora, now dressed up to the nines, strode forward.

'How could you, Nigel? I thought you could ride: your horsemanship is pathetic. Call yourself a gentleman? An English gentleman would never make a bloody fool of himself in front of foreigners.'

There was a brief, pregnant pause, during which Bob muttered, 'But we are Texans.'

My red mist descended. 'And you are no lady; you are just a snob. Superficial status is all you care about because of your sad insecurity over your nouveau riche crook of a father. How dare you screech at me like a fishwife in front of my friends.'

Not surprisingly, I got a reaction: bursting into tears of anger and frustration Pandora stepped up to me and added to my other injuries by punching me right between the eyes. She then turned on her heel and, having shouldered her way through the assembled jeering barflies, disappeared into the general throng.

Phil put a sympathetic arm around me. 'I think you need another drink, old man.'

I wiped my bloody nose and nodded. 'Anything but tequila; that has got me into quite enough trouble for one night.'

As my saviour went off to the bar, Bob returned from the ring with what was left of his severely trampled hat and offered it to me.

'A present for you, Nigel. Do wear it, as with your battered countenance, it will not look out of place.'

I crammed it on my head as I went in search of a rest room to freshen up.

Amazingly, Pandora's expertly delivered right jab had sobered me up and, having switched to drinking beer, I stayed in remarkably good shape until well into the small hours. My companions also paced themselves admirably. Phil managed to fluke some impressive winnings in a chaotic crap game and, by 3 a.m., we were deeply in love with our dancing partners as we smooched to country and western ballads.

We had just canoodled our way into an early breakfast party at Bob's new friend's nearby apartment when my guardian angel gave me a dig in the ribs. Although with my bruised nose and ego the prospect of unfaithful retribution was tempting, in a few hours' time Phil and I had to be at the airport. If we were not, my special plans for the weekend would be put in jeopardy, so the risk of getting carried away was not worth taking.

Leaving Bob with the enviable dilemma of three ladies to sort out, my young partner in crime and I secured a cab to take us back to the hotel. En route, I was asked for the umpteenth time, 'Come on, Nigel, what the hell is our open-ticketed destination later on this morning?'

'Never you mind,' I unhelpfully replied. 'But, in view of your noble conduct last night, my reward will be to help you break free from your recent self-imposed celibacy.'

As we had just arrived at the Fairmont, this remark passed without comment.

Once in the hotel room, in spite of Pandora snoring like a steam engine, I collapsed onto the other queen-sized bed and went straight to sleep, fully dressed.

The eight o'clock breakfast, served in the room, was a tense affair with lots of 'frosties' in evidence! As my hangover made it easy for me to remain mute, it was Pandora who eventually broke the silence.

'If you can bear to stop being a control freak for one moment in your life, I would like you to release my air ticket as I intend to return to London at the earliest possible opportunity.'

I summoned all the sarcasm that I could muster. 'Of course you can have your ticket. However, I insist that you stay over for one more day as Billy Bob's is holding a female amateur boxing contest this evening and I am certain that you could win hands down. Regrettably Phil and I will have to miss the show as we are leaving for Las Vegas this morning on the eleven-thirty flight.'

With a furious glare that would have killed a lesser man, Pandora sprang to her feet, knocking her chair over, and stomped into the bathroom. A resounding crash, even louder than the slamming of the door, heralded the demise of a crystal flower vase and its colourful contents.

In spite of all the histrionics, our trio remained intact as we flew out of Dallas en route for Nevada later that morning.

In true female style, to emphasise that she was still having the vapours, Pandora directed a stream of animated prattle at Phil whilst totally ignoring yours truly. As he was still bursting with euphoria over our recently revealed destination, he seemed quite content to nod and grunt during her pauses for breath. Eventually, though, following a few glasses of wine and a tasty early lunch, she threw in the towel and addressed me.

'I bet you would like to know what I got up to last night.'

'No,' I replied, continuing to read my Wilbur Smith novel.

When dealing with the fair sex, I have always pursued a policy of never showing jealousy or concern over situations which are beyond my control. Though unlikely to deter simple infidelity, I find that this stance undermines the self-justification which many ladies seek before committing a lustful act of retribution. On this occasion, I obviously overplayed my hand as Pandora suddenly burst into tears.

'You don't give a shit about me, do you, you bastard? I try to please you and all you do is humiliate me.'

As Phil discreetly wandered off up the aisle, I responded evenly, 'Listen, I brought you on this trip because I enjoy your company. However, I do not enjoy your company when you are being violent, nagging and sulky. Behave yourself or go home.'

Trying to dry her tears, she said in a small voice, 'I was worried about you. I thought that you had really hurt yourself.'

Being ever a softy at heart, I decided to abandon my overbearing stance. Having tenderly taken her hand in mine, I smilingly kissed her nose and offered her a glass of champagne.

Returning from his short stroll, Phil looked highly relieved that bonhomie had been restored, and gladly accepted some bubbly.

On making my way to the lavatory some moments later, I discovered that, thanks to the previous night's battering, I was obliged to walk rather like a penguin with piles. Also, as the mirror then cruelly reflected, my bruised bulbous red nose closely resembled that of a circus clown. Nevertheless, nothing was now going to stop me maintaining the peace. Having settled back in my seat again, I decided that it was time to make an important announcement.

'It is now time for Phil to put his recent chastity behind him and start having some real fun again before his testosterone turns into tosstestyourown.'

'Really!' said Pandora in mock shock, whilst our guest eyed me uncertainly.

'Nigel, surely women who are on the loose in Las Vegas are in the high-risk category?'

'Not at all; just trust me. I will secure you a date with a girl whose very existence is dependent upon her remaining totally healthy at all times and then you can decide for yourself.'

I was pleased to observe an expression of lascivious anticipation pass across Phil's face.

'You two are such chauvinists,' Pandora said affectionately as the seat belt signs lit up for landing.

Today Las Vegas has developed into a sprawling variety of attractions not that dissimilar to those found at a Disney Park. Twenty-eight years ago, however, most of the top hotels, clubs and casinos were confined to the town's short main street which was known as the Strip. As our plane banked into the final approach for landing, we could clearly see this row of glittering buildings whose hoardings boasted such names as Flamingo, Sands and MGM. These emporia and many like them, had been made famous by stars such as Frank Sinatra, Elvis Presley and others of their genre.

'It almost looks like toytown,' Phil naively remarked.

'There certainly is plenty to play with down there,' I assured him.

As the airport was a stone's throw from the town, it was not long before we arrived at the Hilton hotel. Having tried out various other hostelries over the years and, bearing in mind that one was out most of the time anyway, I found that this one provided the most practical base.

On entering our junior suite, Pandora immediately attributed my choice of accommodation to the 'see yourself as others see you' mirror inside the canopy of the four-poster bed.

'That is nothing compared to the other hotels,' I told her, before swiftly changing tack. 'There is considerable show biz folklore here, though. For instance, it was in this hotel's theatre that the Beatles first rocked America and where Elvis made his famous comeback in 1969.'

I deferred further dialogue as I had to make an urgent phone call to my friend Dick Lebon at his office in Chicago in order to tap into his local influence. As there was a time zone difference, he could be departing for the weekend at any moment and I had a promise to fulfil.

Although the Mafia is generally perceived to be a coercive, corrupt brotherhood, it has always been involved in certain aspects of the American entertainment industry. In 1946, a prominent Don, Bugsy Siegel, chose Las Vegas for the launching of his flamboyantly luxurious Flamingo Hotel complex. In spite of the venture's spectacular success, the entrepreneur was eventually gunned down for his excesses. However, he had set a trend which was to transform an obscure Western town into a thriving, luxury playground, heavily reliant upon Cosa Nostra investment.

The man that I was telephoning, who now ran a successful insurance broking company, had in his younger days worked for an

Italian American property company. Via this earlier involvement and for other more obscure reasons that I had chosen not to probe, he still owned a large stake in the Marlin Club on the Strip.

As it was now late afternoon in Illinois, I was highly relieved when Dick's secretary put my call through. With the quintessential directness of a Jewish Russian immigrant's son, his staccato tones exploded on the line.

'Hey, Nige, how the hell are you? You just caught me and I wouldn't have taken a call from any other guy because I am just about to reap the benefits of my lunch date who is far prettier than you.'

I cut in quickly. 'Hi, Dick, I need a favour.'

This inspired a defensive reaction. 'Now, you're not going to blow out our getting together next weekend. I have got you fixed up with a real doll who is just gagging to meet you.'

I took advantage of his respiration once more. 'Don't worry, what is left of me will catch up with you en route to Montreal, as planned. I am afraid that I have a doll with me and also I have got Phil along for the ride. You remember him, one of Ronald's top honchos?'

'Yep,' Dick affirmed. 'Nice young guy until he gets loaded, then I find him about as much fun as a turd in a punchbowl.'

Having conceded this point, I went on to outline Phil's current pressing needs but, before I could finish, Dick interrupted. 'Nige; if you shut up and clear the line, I will contact Louis at the Marlin and get him to come up with a suitable chick. Give it half an hour, then wander past. Have a great time and I really look forward to catching up with you and the new broad next Friday night. Now blow.'

The call was over.

I had met Louis on numerous occasions before and considered his brusque style of communication to be incompatible with the qualities needed to host a den of iniquity. Nevertheless, Dick assured me that, mainly due to this stolid manager, his investment was run like clockwork and generated impressive returns.

Half an hour later, I was ushered into the Marlin's main salon by a huge black doorman dressed like an Indian Raja. I then soon located the weasel-faced Louis, who was perched on a bar stool, chewing on an unlit cigar with a cocktail in his hand. As usual, he was wearing a chalk-striped double-breasted suit, complimented by a Cagney trilby on the back of his head. Without bothering to stand up or offer me a drink, he jerked his thumb towards the other end of the bar.

'There she is.'

I thanked the hoodlum as I tried to assess a barely discernable female silhouette standing in the penumbra of the bar's oversubtle lighting. Just as I was about to move in for a closer look, Louis's bejewelled hand restrained me.

'Whether or not it's you, whoever the lucky punter is had better be a patient guy. Some of the Mob are due in town and, if that includes Wrangler, the dame will definitely be on call from time to time. For the sake of her own hide, she must phone in here regular.'

He then barked, 'Hazel, get over here.'

Having introduced myself, I concluded the longest conversation that I ever had with Louis and exited with Phil's new friend onto the bustling Friday evening Strip. I had arranged to meet Pandora and Phil in the posthumously named Bugsy's Bar at the Flamingo Hotel, so that was where we were headed. During the short walk, I received numerous envious male glances which obviously related to my companion.

Hazel was clad in a black silk dress that was just short enough to reveal a shapely pair of silk stockinged legs and just tight enough to display the alluring curves of her upper torso. Contrary to the flamboyance displayed by most American woman, she wore no jewellery apart from a short black pearl necklace. This encircled a swanlike neck, above which large blue eyes shone from a classical face haloed by bobbed auburn hair. Although the lady displayed a lively wit, her ingenuous mode of conversation indicated that she was probably still in her teens. Lucky old Phil, damn him!

On our arrival at the rendezvous Phil bounded out of an alcove like an unleashed hound. Pandora was, understandably, less enthusiastic and remained seated in the background. I noted with some amusement that she wore the electric dead-eyed smile on her face that women reserve for would-be rivals.

Anyway, sophisticated or not, Hazel instantly displayed her diplomatic skills. Having acknowledged Phil with cursory interest, she

202

walked straight over to the alcove. I had barely completed formal introductions before she pulled Pandora's fangs by enthusing over her stylish attire and asking about life in London.

I took this opportunity to put my somewhat fidgety young friend in the picture. My good news was that Mafia women had to be clean, or else. My bad news was the Marlin reporting requirement where I suggested that the penalty for non-compliance might be onerous. It was instantly apparent that any objections that Phil may have had to this caveat were instantly dispelled by the impact of Hazel's striking appearance and demeanour.

In order to give the couple time to get to know one another, I whisked Pandora off to the in-house casino which covered an area that would have dwarfed a rugby pitch. When we returned to the bar an hour later and $500 lighter, there was no sign of the lovebirds and I was tersely reminded of my duty.

'You know, Nigel, I am absolutely famished. You have not bothered to feed me since our airborne lunch.'

'OK, Pandora. I tell you what, Jonnie Rabbits is playing at the Sands. Why don't we take in his show whilst we eat something?'

The response was emphatically negative. 'Digesting food to the sound of country and western junketing is the last thing I need, particularly as that ghastly racket would remind me of Fort Worth!'

They just cannot leave it alone sometimes, can they? I moved on swiftly.

'I tell you what; give me half an hour at a blackjack table to win back your roulette disaster and we will have a slap-up dinner at the fabulous roof restaurant here.'

An hour later, with losses now well into four figures, we were ushered to a 'Top Flamingo' window table with a fine view of the kaleidoscope which is Las Vegas after dark. After we had ordered, I called Phil's room at the Hilton and, getting no reply, left a message as to our whereabouts.

It was not until we were rounding off an excellent meal with crêpes Suzette almost two hours later that a liveried flunky presented me with an ornate telephone. Sure enough, it was Phil on the line from the Hilton, who instantly went into raptures.

'If I did not know it was thanks to you, I would have believed that

Hazel was a gift from Heaven. Sorry not to get back to you earlier but I was on another planet. She …'

I interrupted him. 'Phil, please spare me the details. When you have exhausted your cosmic cruising, perhaps you would both like to join us here at the Flamingo for a nightcap.'

'Out of the question, old boy. Hazel called the bloody Marlin and has just had to go off and see some jerk called Wanker or something. She reckoned that she would return in under two hours, so I am not moving from the hotel.'

'Listen to me, Phil,' I said firmly. 'First of all "Wanker" happens to be Wrangler Carvallo, a clever, vicious psychopath who plays for the Mob's first team, so watch your mouth. Secondly, don't count on Hazel being able to fulfil her own time frame. I did warn you that this could happen but, whilst you are waiting, we will come and keep you company. Grab a decent table in the Cabaret Theatre and we can all catch up with the late show.'

On arrival, we located our trooper at a table by the stage. He was obviously compensating for living on the food of love by shovelling down a plate of ham and eggs with hash browns as he half-watched Pavlova and her Pulsating Pythons performing suggestively.

With refreshments on the way, Phil was forced to abandoned his amorous ramblings when Pandora and I deliberately focused our attention on the cabaret. The acts ranged from a tiddly ventriloquist with Purse, his pet alligator, to the corpulent Charley Choice of a Voice who impersonated a string of celebrities we had never heard of. What really made the show, however, was the regular appearance of gorgeously costumed chorus girls who danced with provocative precision to an excellent band with backing singers to match.

A couple of hours later, I was seriously considering calling it a night when Phil, who had hardly taken his eyes off the main entrance, suddenly leapt up in great excitement.

'Well here she is, bang on time, so the chap is a wanker. He obviously has no staying power.'

Without dignifying this crass remark with a response, I got up and welcomed the lovely Hazel. With the resilience of youth, she looked the very picture of fresh innocence, as if she had just attended a parochial church service.

After she had completed her reunion embraces with Phil and settled at the table, I proffered her the night menu before Pandora could move in to catch up on girl talk.

'No thanks, Nigel, I just had a big dinner and I'm stuffed.'

Failing to notice Hazel's inappropriate American terminology, Phil gave me a smug look, so I rather cruelly intoned, 'There is such a thing as room service.'

Much to my relief, as I was still feeling the effects of the night before, after the next bottle of fizz was drained Pandora suggested that we all hit the sack. Phil needed no prompting, so we proceeded to set a new early-to-bed record in the town that never sleeps.

Next morning, after a late start, my escort insisted that we spend the day enjoying as many Las Vegas sights and experiences as possible. Playing guide was fine with me, but just prior to leaving I almost got wrong-footed over a surprise that I had organised.

'By the way, Nigel, while you were in the bath this morning, a chap called Roy Poss phoned and said to tell you that everything is OK for tomorrow. What are you up to?'

I swatted the question by saying that it was just a client confirming delivery of a ship. In truth, Roy was a helicopter pilot whose background included stunt flying in the *M*A*S*H* television soap and training gunship pilots in Vietnam.

Phil had called earlier to say that his inamorata had been 'Wrangled' again for lunch and the afternoon, but would return before we were due to attend the MGM Supper Show. I had booked this extravaganza under extreme pressure from Pandora. My objection was that it starred Liberace, the mincing pianist who had made many of us puke whilst our mums swooned over his antics during his UK tour in the 1950s!

Somewhat to my relief, lover boy was not joining us during the day as he wanted to spend time alone and do some shopping.

'Don't go blowing a fortune on her,' I warned.

'It won't be as much as you two have wasted on the tables,' was the trite reply.

During our excursion, an incident occurred that would have devastated Phil, and brought home to me once again what a cruel and wicked world we all live in.

After lunch, Pandora insisted that we visit Caesar's Palace and, whilst ascending the marble walkway flanked by statues of the Roman deity, we ran into a small cavalcade.

Preceded by a legion of lackeys, trundling tasselled trolleys loaded with luxurious leather luggage, strode a gaunt giant of a man. He was dressed entirely in black except for a yellow tie which almost matched his shoulder-length hair. Although his scarred face was partly concealed by oversized shades, he appeared to be in his middle years but, judging by his lithe movements, he was obviously still in good shape. This also applied to the mature but sleek blonde beauty on his arm. They were flanked by four thick-set, dark-suited men who wore the haunted scowl that is so often evident on the faces of men with violent callings.

As the entourage swept past, heading for a couple of parked stretch limousines, I buttonholed one of the hotel staff not involved in the procession.

'Who the hell is that?'

The flunky regarded me incredulously. 'Wrangler Carvallo, of course. He's leaving for LA early, and judging by his looks, he ain't happy.'

I turned gloatingly to an obviously perplexed Pandora.

'My God, Hazel has aged since we last saw her. Why do you ladies always strive to turn mendacity and deception into an art form?'

'We take lessons from rascals like you,' she laughingly replied, obviously intrigued by this chance encounter.

Having moved on to explore the monolithic mock-up of ancient Rome, we eventually ended up with the plebs in the one-armed bandit hall. Unbelievably, Pandora's frantic coin feeding was suddenly rewarded with a $2,500 minor jackpot. This more than recouped our earlier, more sophisticated losses so, as gambling is not one of my vices, I insisted that we quit whilst we were ahead.

We returned to the Hilton in good time to get ready for my forthcoming ordeal at MGM's vast, ornate dining theatre. Whilst we were doing so, Phil phoned up, as happy as a sand boy, because Hazel had just returned.

'Don't you dare say anything,' was urgently mouthed at me by Pandora as I arranged rendezvous details with him.

Reluctantly, I had to admit that Liberace's show turned out to be tremendous entertainment, for which I had to suffer a lot of 'told you so' ribbing. I was further teased over sharing part of my surname with the impresario's boyfriend, who, dressed as a chauffeur drove him onto the stage in a red Rolls-Royce, to open the show.

Despite the extreme diversity of their backgrounds, Hazel and Pandora had become firm friends, which helped to make our final evening in Las Vegas thoroughly enjoyable.

Before saying good night, I addressed our small group. 'It is sad that some of us have to fly off to San Francisco tomorrow evening but, before then, I have planned a treat that you are all unlikely to forget.'

In spite of intense pestering, I refused to divulge any further information except that, at 2.30 p.m. on the morrow, a limousine would pick us up outside the hotel's main entrance to take us to an undisclosed destination.

Whilst awaiting breakfast in the room the next morning, I slipped out on the pretext of trying to find a recent edition of an English newspaper and was soon dialling out on a lobby payphone.

'Hi Roy, I got your message, which almost blew the surprise. Just confirming it's all stations go for our 3 p.m. trip this afternoon.'

The receiver boomed out the pilot's enthusiastic response. 'That's terrific, Nigel. So sorry for any indiscretion and I am really looking forward to seeing you again.'

I bid Roy a fond farewell and returned for breakfast, *sans* journal.

Later on, shortly before we were due to embark on the mystery tour, I was to suffer a potential mutiny from the ever-turbulent Phil. The problem emanated from the fact that he had obviously fallen head over heals in love with Hazel, who had been obliged to absent herself again during the morning.

When the lad failed to appear for the limousine pick-up as planned, I phoned his room from the lobby and, with extreme self-restraint, politely inquired as to why. The answer was not encouraging.

'Nigel, I really must beg you to excuse us from attending your surprise outing. Hazel returned only half and hour ago and we need maximum time together before I leave with you two tonight.'

My tether's end had been reached. 'Phil, you know that I am the one man in the world who is most likely to sympathise with your romantic sense of priorities. That said, I have invested a considerable amount of money on your behalf and you are endeavouring to repay me by behaving like a spoilt child. We are already ten minutes late, so, both of you, kindly get down here immediately!'

I banged down the house phone with sufficient force to make several passers-by jump and, within a matter of minutes, I got the desired result. However, as the recalcitrant couple sheepishly emerged from a nearby lift, I was a little taken aback at Hazel's revealing attire. Whilst it was totally suitable for teasing and pleasing in the boudoir, it was deliciously inappropriate for my forthcoming plans. But, what the hell.

Following a breakneck 20-minute drive, we arrived at the heliport where numerous hoardings promoting Grand Canyon excursions soon blew the secrecy of the outing. Although the accolades of appreciation I then received from my companions were slightly muted with apprehension, little did they guess what was really in store for them.

On alighting from the elongated transport, we were immediately greeted by our stocky host, Roy Poss. Bursting with his customary bonhomie, he bounced out of the Bower Helicopters office and greeted me with a growling bear hug. Then, having shaken Phil's hand, he took his time introducing himself to the girls, especially Hazel, whom he openly stood back and admired.

'I see that you are wearing your parachute already!'

With no further ado, we were ushered towards a compact red helicopter which was already being noisily warmed up by a member of the ground crew. Roy then helped us up a slender flight of steps into the generously windowed fuselage where we settled ourselves into the snug seating arrangements.

Having replaced the mechanic at the controls and swiftly acquainted everyone with the safety rules and procedures, our pilot then gave us exaggerated thumbs-up sign. What followed was, in my opinion, the most inappropriate public relations exercise ever contrived. However, Roy insisted on delivering his passenger briefings as he saw fit and claimed that no one had run off yet.

'You see this, all of you? This thumb is like a Roman Emperor's in that, whilst it points at the heavens, everybody lives. To bear witness to this, I have been involved in three major accidents during my long chopper flying career and this small scar on my thumb represents my only wound.

'Contrary to popular belief, the contraption that you are about to fall in love with is not a flying brick. Should the engine dare to fail, all I have to do is freewheel the rotor like a bicycle and set down in the nearest safe place. Any questions?'

Not surprisingly, curiosity was locked up as tightly as everyone's buttocks!

When all seat belts had been fastened, we lurched into the air and soon passed over the Hoover Dam's vast white edifice at the base of Lake Mead. After about 50 minutes' flying, the broken scrubland below became decidedly more undulating and it seemed that we were embracing every contour. I knew from past experience that this flight pattern was all part of a dramatic build-up.

Sure enough, whilst rapidly closing on some prominent ridges, Roy casually turned towards us and chatted over the intercom about the wild burros that roamed the slopes beneath. I watched with fascination whilst my fellow passengers' mild interest dissolved into stark horror as a bizarre test of nerves developed. Who would be first to point out that we appeared to be heading straight for a craggy wall that was looming ominously ahead of us?

Phil was the first to crack. 'For Christ's sake, look where you are bloody well going before you kill us all!'

Having regarded the 'chicken' with contempt, our pilot un-hurriedly faced forward, as our machine skimmed over the escarpment and, in an instant, we entered a different world.

Actually, in spite of the bowel-churning anxiety it had caused, there was some method in Roy's apparent madness. His stealthy approach cleverly maximised the visual impact of the world's most famous canyon which suddenly spread before us like some vast iridescent layered cake. However, our appreciation of this majestic geographical panorama was to be short-lived. No sooner had we debouched into the void over a mile above Grand Canyon's floor than, to the strains of Richard Wagner's 'Ride of the Valkyries', we went into a plunging descent.

With the rapidly widening image of the Colorado River rushing up to meet us like a bloating snake, I was pleased to observe that everyone was settling into the spirit of things. As the girls screamed orgasmic encouragement, Phil went into paroxysms of semi-hysterical mirth. However, a sudden silence reigned, as Roy pulled out of his free fall and streaked along the river at full throttle, not more than 12 feet above its surface. The aerobatics which then ensued, as we flew closely between, over and around rock formations protruding from the water, kept everyone's heart in their mouths, including me.

We were on a section of the river which had an acutely winding course and it was whilst banking around a particularly sharp bend that we found ourselves almost on top of a raft. The 15 or so passengers were clad in nothing but the tufts that God had granted them and our sudden appearance had obviously shocked and irritated them. They immediately made this abundantly clear via a general salute of fingers and bums.

I had witnessed similar adventurers before, whose idea of having a good time was to sail down the Colorado River from its upper reaches in basic craft. Apart from sharing hazardous conditions, particularly through the rapids, landing opportunities were rare due to Indian reservation privacy rights. Thus, as these folk could be confined in each others' company in primitive conditions for days on end, their only compensation was that intimacy could easily develop.

Having subjected the nomadic mariners to a final pass, which pleased them no more than our first effort, we continued upriver with our pilot continuing to put us through more high jinks.

As we zoomed past an unexpected plateau, Pandora got very excited on spotting an Indian encampment and begged Roy to land so that we could take a closer look.

'Too dangerous,' was the unequivocal reply.

Phil then unwisely decided to put his oar in. 'Why not? There is plenty of space and I am sure the natives would just love to meet us. Lost your nerve or something?'

I knew the real reason for the refusal, and it is only my scrupulous honesty which prevents me from claiming the story first hand.

210

Anyway, before I could tell Phil to stop behaving like a prick, Roy cut in crisply.

'Listen, what's your name, my nerve is never in question; I just don't want to put *three* decent lives plus my own in danger. The territory down there belongs to the Navajo "natives", as you choose to patronisingly call them, and they cherish their territorial rights.

'Three years ago, whilst with a party of your countrymen I landed quite near here to fix a door fastening. I was just done when a whole bunch of Indians arrived on the rocks above and, with no warning, opened up a fusillade. We all high-tailed it sharply before anybody was hurt or the 'copter got shot up.

'You can't beat the British sublime optimism, though. The guy in charge of the party congratulated me all the way back to base for putting on such a fine show, then gave me a fifty dollar tip. An American customer would have sued my ass!'

Phil's profuse apologies appeared to have been fully accepted as our pilot lifted us up out of the canyon and eventually landed on top of a small mountain in the Arizona wilderness.

Having shut down the rotors, Roy invited us to alight and stretch our legs whilst he disappeared behind some nearby boulders. Assuming that he was just taking a pee break, my three friends were somewhat bemused when our trusty shepherd reappeared with a small round table. Having covered it with a red chequered cloth, he departed once more, returning this time with a bottle of Krug in an ice bucket and five glasses on a tray. He also carried a camera.

Simon, one of my sons, still retains copies of the photographs taken that day in front of the chopper which, for reasons of discretion, I gave to him for safe-keeping years ago. Phil, who is now a big shot in the banking industry, chooses to believe that Simon's boasted possession of this material is just a wind-up. In view of the diaphanously clad young lady who is depicted kissing him in some of the pictures, it would be cruel to disillusion him!

Pandora and I were never destined for a meaningful relationship, which was probably just as well for her sake.

To this day Phil fondly remembers his magic moments with Hazel. It is only to be hoped that, with her wit, charm and grace, she eventually managed to emerge happily from her demanding profession.

10

The Little White Cloud That Cried

He said that he was very lonely,
Didn't care if he lived or died.
That's why I will always remember
The little white cloud that cried.

Unbelievably, the above words, including the title, are from a 1950s hit song which was sung by the rather emasculated, half-deaf American singer, Johnny Ray. He was among the better-known artists who epitomised the meandering post-war pop star genre prior to the spectacular and enduring advent of rock and roll. It was to be many years before I got an inkling of what the bizarre lyrics of this particular rendering by Mr Ray really meant.

'Nige, this opportunity is far too big to miss so we just have to pull it off at all costs.'

As Dick Marcovich's shrewd dark eyes twinkled mischievously over the rim of his Vodka Martini, I raised my similarly charged glass in salutation.

'When I have sorted out the labour pains in London, I shall rely on you to deliver the baby over here in the States.'

A set of perfectly capped teeth smiled. 'I am most flattered by your sublime confidence in me, but let's cut the bullshit for a moment. With the awkward bastard that we are dealing with, it will be a caesarean section that will need both our delivery skills.'

I smiled confidently at my friend of many years, whose career I had followed with admiration as he skilfully built up his highly successful specialist insurance agency in New York.

Being the son of a Latvian Jewish immigrant, Dick had forged his fortune via the unpaved route but, when the money came rolling in, only the best would do for his wife and family. Otherwise, however, the man was a total enigma. When he was not vigorously pursuing his business interests, he switched his obsessive energy into assuming the role of a playboy. Sadly, the shrewdness that he demonstrated in commerce was in stark contrast to his crass ineptitude when playing the bon viveur.

Setting aside boozing and gambling, my friend's cardinal flaw was sexual dyslexia. Never seeming to comprehend the difference between lust and love, Dick would insist on buying what most men occasionally rent. This penchant led to his furtively supporting a succession of expensive hookers, mainly recruited from London's smarter nightclubs. In fact, the main reason that we were meeting at San Francisco's Mark Hopkins Hotel, was because Jenny, his latest import from Soho, was living in one of his apartments nearby.

I ordered more drinks. 'So, maestro, you think that we should give Rudi the full treatment with a choir and cherubs?'

Rudolph Bartelli was a key senior executive at All American Mutual Assurance, the company to whom we intended to sell an ingenious, but expensive, protection programme. Although very able, he was a petulant confirmed bachelor whose volatile personality needed kid-glove handling.

Dick looked through me thoughtfully. 'We need to make a presentation on neutral territory of our choosing, followed by a lavish dinner at an impressive, but not vulgar, venue. Like most amateur proctologists, Rudi is a frightful snob.'

After a short pause, Dick's eyes lit up with inspiration. 'Bingo. I've got it. The Beverly Wilshire in Hollywood fits the bill to perfection. What do you say, Nige?'

'It's one hell of a journey from Washington.'

I was regarded sceptically. 'You are not thinking straight. The location is our trump card. A guy with Rudi's habits will jump at an opportunity to spend time in California, let alone Hollywood, with all expenses paid. Anyway, Nige, you should know that it's a perfect rendezvous, you spent enough time there recently.'

This was true; the previous year one of my senior operatives had stumbled upon a promising business opportunity in Beverly Hills. As this was uncharted territory for me, I had abused my position as his boss and insisted upon overseeing the project personally, with the Beverly Wilshire Hotel as my base.

In all honesty, the few visits I then made to 'Tinseltown' were somewhat of a disappointment. The only famous show business personality that I encountered was the octogenarian George Burns, who appeared to be a permanent fixture in the hotel bar.

This charismatic ex-vaudeville comic's most recent claim to fame had been *The Burns and Allen Show*, a TV top favourite during the 1950s and 1960s. When the series tragically ended, due to his wife Gracie Allan's demise, the Hollywood scandal sheets reported that, from then on, George had never stopped falling from grace!

I have to admit that this heartless observation appeared to be true. Whenever I met him, he always had a drink in his hand, a cigar in his mouth and, in spite of his 'rug'-crowned, wrinkled little body, slinky nymphets were ever in attendance.

Anyway, in spite of my past disillusionment with the venue, I could see by the set of my friend's jaw that he had made his mind up over the meeting whether I liked it or not.

'OK, Dick, I am with you, the Beverly Wilshire it is, but, for God's sake, book rooms in the new wing; the old building is falling apart.'

Further discussion was obviated by the arrival of the stunning Jenny, accompanied by my date for the evening, Rubenesque Gwen whose company I had enjoyed on a previous occasion. After hugs, kisses and more cocktails, we switched into self-destruct mode and hit the town.

Three weeks later, by which time I had tied up the London end of our project, Dick phoned me at my office.

'Right, Nige, the good news is that we are all stations go for the Hollywood presentation at six p.m. next Thursday. The bad news is that Rudi's chief happens to be visiting the LA branch next week and insists on attending the meeting.'

I cursed under my breath. 'Now that sounds like a real pain in the arse. Although I have yet to meet the great Burt O'Farrell, I understand from those who have, that he is a right bastard.'

'You have heard correctly,' Dick confirmed. 'But you don't build up a multi-million-dollar business by being Mr Nice Guy. Having said that, on the two occasions I met him, if you dig deep, a glimmer of good humour can be found. Better still, this tends to blossom with bourbon, to which Burt is particularly partial. Our main problem is that he hates Brits, particularly obvious ones like you.'

It is one of the strange anomalies of the New World in that the American Irish are far more aggressively nationalistic than the folk back home. This also applies to the Scots and the French Canadians.

'Well, if only because of our boarding school system, with his proclivities Rudi has got to be an Anglophile. Get him to emphasise to Burt that I am from Catholic stock, which usually helps with the Irish,' I suggested.

'With one obvious exception, Rudi will like everything his boss likes,' Dick countered. 'Just try to play yourself down for a change Nige, there is a shit load of commission at stake here.

'I have booked The Wilshire's most swanky private dining room for our presentation, with dinner afterwards. I will see you there; keep in touch.'

He hung up.

Infuriatingly, my Kennedy/LAX flight the following Thursday was running an hour late which meant that I was tight on time for the Beverly Wilshire appointment. In view of this, I saved some precious moments by changing into a light blue seersucker suit whilst awaiting the delayed take-off.

Fortunately, as this was a short trip, I was only carrying hand luggage and had already organised a Chrysler convertible with immediate availability at the arrivals Avis desk. My choice of car was totally contrived as, combined with the Southern politician-style attire, I felt that this would play down my Englishness.

Following some frustrating stacking prior to landing, my flight ended up another 15 minutes late, so by the time I signed for the car I was in a perspiring, winded panic. My haste was to cost me dearly as, when the Avis agent explained the car's controls, I paid no attention whatsoever. However, I was pleased to observe that the red convertible's roof was down.

Although the lady was a tramp who said that California was cold and damp, everybody knows that it is invariably warm and the sun always shines; well, almost always.

With precious minutes ticking away, I cursed as I became snarled up in rush hour traffic. Then, just to really make my day, as I crawled along Santa Monica Boulevard I distinctly felt a large raindrop strike my face from an apparently cloudless sky. Looking up in astonishment, I spotted him, the little white cloud that was cheekily hovering overhead and, boy, did he cry. Within moments torrents rained down with monsoon intensity. Obviously, my first reaction was to put up the automatic roof, but how? Apart from having ignored the briefing, I have always been intimidated by anything remotely mechanical. By the time I had randomly pressed a few knobs to no avail, I had reached the optimum state of saturation anyway. As I eventually reached the Beverly Hills turn-off, the car was actually filling up with water when, his job done, my nimbus tormentor departed to drench alternative pastures.

On entering the Wilshire gateway, I had but five minutes to spare before I was supposed to be on parade. My only option was to check in as swiftly as possible, do a lightning change into my one spare suit, then immediately locate and join the presentation party. The best-laid plans of mice and men …!

Unfortunately Dick had arranged for everyone to congregate in the hotel's lounge bar which happened to overlook the forecourt and main entrance. Thus, when I sloshed my way out of the Chrysler clutching my hand luggage, I received a nasty surprise. Regarding me from a nearby large bay window with drinks in their hands was a smartly dressed group of people whose expressions ranged from bemused to horrified. Unfortunately Dick and Rudi were foremost among the latter category.

Deciding that I would just have to brazen things out as best I could, I was to discover that someone up there liked me, after all. As I squelched into reception, I was approached by a dapper little middle-aged man with a pugnacious, lantern-jawed countenance from which glared dark, penetrating eyes.

'I have reason to believe that you are Nigel Kemble-Clarkson. I am Bert O'Farrell. So what are you after, a sympathy vote?'

My heart sank as, for a change, I was tongue-tied.

'Let me give you a piece of advice, young man; when you go for a swim in a light suit, do not wear dark blue undershorts, it looks kind of tacky.'

Then, much to my surprise and delight, the tycoon burst into fits of booming laughter. 'If it is one thing I love to see, it is a humiliated Englishman.'

His hilarity was sycophantically echoed by Rudi and a small entourage of his senior staff who had gathered behind him, accompanied by a much-relieved Dick.

Trying not to drip water on the immaculate blue suit and gleaming loafers, I accepted Bert's proffered handshake. Following a vice-like attempt to fracture my fingers, he then turned to the assembled company.

'And now if the man from Atlantis would like to change out of his diving gear, maybe we can get the dog and pony show out of the way and concentrate our energies on some serious partying. I have taken the liberty of inviting some ambitious wannabe starlets along later on and we would not wish to keep them waiting, would we? I am in a philanthropic mood tonight.'

Unbeknown to me, the deal was probably all done bar the shouting as Bert had already formed a favourable impression with our preliminary report. However, my eccentric entrance had certainly done our cause no harm at all and Dick was over the moon when the order was officially confirmed later that evening.

And so it came to pass that the tears of the little white cloud were turned to laughter.

11

Pool of Tears

In spite of the fact that I met the shipowner Einar Gronholm only twice in person, he has to be the most atypical Norwegian that I have ever encountered. His diminutive, swarthy form was crowned by a shock of black curls, complemented by a luxuriant chest embellished with gilded chains. When not concealed behind tortoiseshell shades, his dark brown eyes twinkled with a sardonic guile which belied his dazzlingly boyish smile. Although he rarely ventured north of Monaco and the Oslo office was simply a front for his Bahrain operation, he loved to boast about his Viking origins.

In addition to his personal image inconsistencies, Einar was a poor maritime icon as his ships seemed to suffer from a distinct lack of buoyancy. In the early 1980s, with an old ten-vessel fleet, already plagued by misfortune, he managed to rack up three total losses in the space of ten months. A sinister aspect of this streak of bad luck was that it coincided with the shipowner's imminent obligation to pay for four brand new tankers. To add insult to injury for his insurers, Gronholm had recently renamed his ships following his scandalous divorce from a Danish heiress in favour of a Turkish cabaret dancer. Lloyd's had therefore been obliged to pay out millions of dollars for the demise of *Belly Dancer*, *Belly Rocker* and *Belly Jiver*. It was at this nadir of Einar's credibility that I was brought into the picture by Eric Strand, one of my broking contacts in Oslo.

A popular saying in the north of England is, 'Where there's muck, there's brass'. There never was a truer saying and it certainly applies big time to the insurance industry. 'Mucky' clients attract meaty premiums which generate lots of commission 'brass' for negotiators like me.

I was, therefore, delighted to take on the challenge of securing cover for a shipowner whose loss pattern should, in theory, have rendered him uninsurable. In spite of this, though, I felt confident that, if handled properly, my entrepreneurial underwriting friend Ronald Pool could be persuaded to pick up this gauntlet. Not only did the Welshman love the challenge of involving himself with oddball characters, but also I was sure that he was dying to learn more about the owner's prototype product tankers. In addition, as our trade is in many ways similar to bookmaking, I was confident that I would be able to 'lay off' some of the more hazardous risk aspects. Nevertheless, the game was very much afoot until the underwriter was won over.

'You must be bloody joking, Nigel. I wouldn't touch that little shit's fleet with a ten-foot barge pole and that's it,' was Ronald's opening reaction as he squeezed his 280-pound bulk into a Short's Tavern alcove.

This was a disappointing start to the lunch, so I feigned wounded indignation.

'Come on, be reasonable; his last total loss was no more than bad luck. The Greek pilot was to blame for parking the *Belly Jiver* on a rock.'

'Bollocks. The chap was probably bribed. However, what really sticks in my craw is that Gronholm is using underwriters' money to pay for his four new vessels. They are an interesting design, though; when are the deliveries scheduled?'

'Three of them within the year,' I casually replied.

The float had bobbed and the line had flexed, which was sufficient for openers. Thus, I deliberately discussed other matters for the rest of the meal whilst Ronald played kneesy under the table as alcohol put him in touch with his female side.

Following a wheezing ascent of the cellar restaurant's stairs after lunch, his resolve cracked.

'Find out the exact dates of the Gronholm deliveries plus whether the tanks are stainless steel or bitumen coated and then I might be interested. Only in the new vessels; not the old crap.'

I wagged my finger. 'Forget it. No cream without the crap.'

Ronald chuckled fatly, choosing to misinterpret my remark as a double entendre. 'Find out anyway. You can let me know when I see you tomorrow evening for our weekly LOH contract meeting.'

As I was in a state of matrimony at the time, I fielded a caution. 'I have a dinner party at home tomorrow evening, so I cannot hang around too long. Mainly thanks to you, I have had sufficient frosties for breakfast this year to last me a lifetime.'

Subsequent to the birth of their much-cherished daughter, the Pool marriage had degenerated into a pattern of stagnant indifference. This meant that quality time for Ronald was spent away from home, preferably after dark, which boded ill for the domestic stability of his friends and business associates. Thus, his response to my caveat was predictably unsympathetic.

'The amount of time that you are prepared to spend in solving your Troll problem is entirely your decision. I didn't ask to be pushed into a sellers' market.'

'You think that you have got me by the balls, don't you, Ronald? We shall have to see about that, you old bastard, but please do try to be a little more commercially grown up when we meet tomorrow.'

Having laughingly bid each other a fond farewell, I was sufficiently optimistic to phone Eric and tell him that there was a glimmer of light at the end of our very dark tunnel. I also insisted that no other brokers were put on the case. Amateur tampering spells disaster when an expert is at work.

On my arrival at six on the dot for the following evening's meeting, Ronald was standing at his desk in the middle of a phone call. Waving me to a chair, he clamped the receiver under his jowls as he poured two huge measures of whisky into plastic cups and signalled me to add ice and water. Ten minutes later, when he had finished screaming at Paulo Mitolo, he perspiringly plonked his bulky body into an equally overstuffed revolving leather chair.

'F***ing Wops, I don't know why I bother.'

Having been responsible for an Italian operation in my previous job, I smiled sympathetically. 'Oh yes you do. If you can accept being paid late and go along with a modicum of mendacity, they are great fun to deal with. Also, like me, you adore the Italian Riviera, especially Porto Fino.'

Running his fingers through his mop of black hair, Ronald wobbled his chins at me. 'All true, Nigel, but if you are in a rush, let's get on as I have several matters to discuss with you in addition to the LOH contract.'

'Such as the Gronholm marine insurances,' I put in forcefully.

'On reflection, I really don't think that we will have time to discuss that matter this evening. Anyway, I am going to need a great deal of persuading before I even consider any form of commitment.'

So this was to be the game. If the fat cat thought that he could turn my quest into a *Tom and Jerry* cartoon, I was determined to disappoint him.

An hour later, having discussed a number of projects whilst we ingested most of the Scotch, Ronald gave out his regular 'end of meeting' signal by commencing to polish his leather desk top with Pledge.

'Well, Nigel, mustn't keep your little lady and the guests waiting too long, so we had better call it a night.'

I deliberately affected a look of aggravated frustration, which produced the desired result.

'Of course, if you are prepared to buy me some dinner at the White Elephant Club, I might view your Nordic cause more sympathetically.'

Having now received a nod and a wink, with time before expiry of the current fleet insurances fast running out, I had no option but to accede.

My reaction from the home front over the telephone was graphically to the point and thankfully brief. Frosties were definitely back on the breakfast menu!

Following a swift one for the road, Ronald and I easily secured a cab in Leadenhall Street and were soon ensconced in the comfortable surroundings of the White Elephant's bar. As with Annabel's and the Carlton, I was not a bona fide club member. However, my frequent appearances at these venues over the years, plus bravado and tactical tipping, had rendered such a formality superfluous.

In spite of just having polished off half a bottle of Scotch, my rotund guest insisted on quaffing his mandatory two 'rusty nails' whilst we considered the menu. Meanwhile, knowing that I needed to retain a modicum of sobriety until my objective was achieved, I made slow work of a large Tio Pepe.

One of the main reasons why Ronald favoured this club was because it was a popular haunt of certain show business personalities. I was, therefore, obliged to shelve my cause again when he became totally preoccupied as Frankie Howerd was ushered into the bar accompanied by a slender young male.

'How come a funny man looks so bloody depressed?' my guest remarked.

I had run into the famous Mr Howerd on a few previous occasions. 'He always does. Apart from hating his wig-maker, in common with many comedians, when he is not striving for his next laugh, he languishes in a miserable twilight world between tension and booze.'

'He probably drinks less than you do,' observed Ronald rather unkindly.

I fired right back from the hip. 'Yes, but I have to make miserable buggers like you laugh. Now when can we talk about fixing terms for my problem fleet, Ronald? I really am finding your procrastination most irritating.'

'Do stop going on so, Nigel. I have decided to help you but I shall do so in my own time. Oh look! Frankie has got his hand on that guy's knee.'

Having at last got a declaration of intent, I decided not to push my luck, particularly as Ronald was getting into a volatile mood, which was a regular feature of his drinking.

Much to my relief, the morose comic, having managed to upset his cocktail, muttered some decidedly unfunny expletives and departed, followed by his tearful playmate. At last I thought that a window had opened for me to develop my proposal, but this was not to be so.

'Let's eat now, Nigel, I am absolutely famished.'

On adjourning to the dining room, we were rewarded with a celebrity spot replacement. Three tables away from us was Bruce Forsyth, escorted by his biggest 'Brucie Bonus' to date, the statuesque beauty, Anthea Redfern.

Ronald glowered at the couple. 'I do not understand how he gets away with it. He is the same age as me, damn him!'

'Probably because he is more cooperative and generous than you are,' I cut in pointedly.

This promoted a gloating chuckle from my guest. 'OK, keep your shirt on, I will sort you out when I have been fed.'

Sadly, due to the coincidence of our bearing witness to a second show business sense of humour failure in one evening, my great matter was to be deferred.

Following an excellent dinner, copiously complimented by fine wines, I was removing papers from my pocket to discuss over the Armagnac when all hell broke loose. Ms Redfern sprang to her feet and the couple exchanged insults for what seemed like an eternity.

Diners and staff were transfixed by this cabaret and, with my sense of humour exaggerated by booze, I decided to instigate a round of applause. This received sporadic support from other tables as Anthea stormed out and Bruce tottered off to complete drowning his sorrows at the bar. 'Didn't she do well?'

Ronald, who had not applauded, regarded me grimly. 'Your clapping is not remotely amusing, Nigel. I happen to be a big Forsyth fan and you are just kicking a man when he is down. You can stuff your lousy business.'

Although I slightly regretted my insensitivity, dignity has to be maintained at all times. 'You pompous arshole. I have been dicked around all the evening and now you have found a pathetic excuse to go back on your word. I am leaving and you can go and screw yourself!'

Ronald and I had spats like this quite often so, as I waved for the bill, somewhat to my relief, he put a restraining hand on my knee.

'Hey, not so fast; I am supposed to be the prima donna around here. I tell you what, though, seeing Redfern all flushed with her breasts heaving has made me feel frisky. We can just make the last show at the Swallow if we get a move on, and I will give you your precious quote at my flat afterwards'

My high perch was instantly abandoned, particularly as Ronald was advocating a visit to my favourite bordello, and we were on our way.

Since my early twenties I had always regarded the Swallow Club in Piccadilly as the ideal haven for relaxation after a hard day's work. An added attraction was that it also provided an environment where beautiful young ladies were given the opportunity to earn tax-efficient income.

The maître d', who selflessly orchestrated this women's liberation forum whilst also overseeing the sale of excessively priced alcohol and indifferent cuisine, was called Rudi. To be fair, this incorrigible rogue, who looked just like a moustachioed villain from the silent movie era, was an incredibly smooth operator. Sadly, however, due to his oversubtle accounting methods, he was sometimes absented from his duties to spend time at Her Majesty's pleasure. Perversely, it was an affront to royalty which was to eventually bring him down.

In the late 1980s an article appeared in a Sunday rag entitled 'Queen lives on immoral earnings'. This did not relate to some middle-aged fairy renting out his drainage system. The focus of the report was that the Swallow Club and several other questionable club venues were located on real estate which ultimately belonged to the Crown. Even though the story was erroneous, Rudi's image suffered irreparable damage. From being tolerated and patronised by the establishment and elements of the constabulary, he had suddenly become a pariah. This meant that erstwhile 'blind eyes' turned hostile and, by the end of the 1990s, the Swallow and certain other similar nightspots were frozen out of existence.

Anyway, as Ronald and I arrived that evening – the best of friends once again – Rudi was still very much in his heyday. Having greeted us with excessive enthusiasm, he then conducted us to a table in prime position for watching the cabaret, which was just commencing. As the usual cavalcade of laddered stockings and leery jokes got under way, Ronald's attention wandered to an adjacent table. This was occupied by a gaggle of lady guests who were drinking together whilst awaiting selection.

'You see that fabulous blonde in the long green dress, Nigel?'

I nodded enthusiastically, as she did, indeed, look most appealing as she chatted and giggled with her companions.

'If you want to ensure the best of my goodwill, I suggest that you invite her to join us. Why not grab someone for yourself whilst you are at it?'

I was almost tempted. 'It's all very well for you, Ronald, with your wife in the country. I am sufficiently in the shit already, but I will certainly get Goldilocks to join us.'

Normally I would have got a waiter to effect procurement but, as none was at hand, I strolled over to the table myself. Immediately the quarry greeted me I knew that trouble was looming. Unlike many instant friends from the twilight world, she bore up well to closer scrutiny. However, as I bent forward to address her, I was assailed by a gust of breath that reeked like a pub carpet at closing time.

'So what's up big boy?' was her highly original opening line which was delivered in a slurred Irish brogue.

Adapting my mode of address to allow for her obviously diminished mental age, I spelt out, 'I am Nigel and I want you to come over and meet my friend Ronald, who is a much bigger boy than me.'

'Well, my name is Alice, I come from Dublin and, as your friend looks like the Emperor Nero, I am bringing three friends with me so that we can have a Roman orgy.'

By now she had managed, with some difficulty, to get to her feet so, having declined her gregarious proposal, I guided her to the table. As she waved her friends goodbye I gingerly engineered her stumbling body into what little space was available beside Ronald.

'My oh my, he is a really big boy,' she exclaimed as she received a slobbering kiss on her left shoulder.

Sexual finesse had never been Ronald's strong suit and he missed a great deal by regarding the fair sex as receptacles for self-gratification without really understanding them. However, whilst the two lust birds got to know each other, I sought out mine host to establish some ground rules.

'Hey, Rudi, we are leaving soon, so make sure that your notional minimum deposit fee is on the bill. Until then, unless you want puke all over the place, Alice is not to be offered any food. Also, only serve her the diluted champagne that you reserve for the Arabs and Japanese. Meanwhile, Ronald and I will polish off the remains of that incredibly expensive bottle of Glenfiddich that you are holding from the last time you ripped me off.'

Rudi stepped back in mock devastation, his evil dark eyes twinkling with mirth. 'Fine, Nigel. Alice's drinking and drugging is starting to piss me off but she is a genius in the sack: I know from my test run!'

With a glance of feigned disdain, I said, 'You really are a totally hopeless case,' and returned to the table to see how Cupid was faring with his incongruous mission.

In keeping with her Gaelic heritage, our new guest was a good-natured boozer and appeared to have reached the happy state of totally losing her inhibitions. However, the commercial autopilot was still managing to function.

'I tell you what, Ronald and Nigel, with your silly names to keep me laughing, at a small additional cost, how about a threesome?'

My 'I think not' and Ronald's 'Why not' were simultaneous.

Alice faked a pout, with her lower lip protruding ridiculously 'What's the matter, Nigel, are you scared of me?'

'No, I am scared of him!' I bellowed laughingly above a cabaret chorus crescendo.

Mercifully, our lurid conversation was drowned by an Abba number, to which scantily clad beauties mimed and danced. When this ended, I instigated my customary heckling exchange with the rather overprecious compère, Dickey, and came second by a short head.

As the floor show concluded with a blaring finale, Ronald suddenly seemed eager to depart for his Bayswater Road apartment as soon as possible. He was obviously anxious to advance his relationship with Alice, which suited me as I was equally keen to get my deal agreed and get home to Fulham for some rest and recuperation.

For the London base of a wealthy man, Ronald's seedy third-floor, one-bedroom flat was pretty pathetic. On our arrival, Alice, who had been jabbering rubbish ever since we left the nightclub, was ordered to shut up and relax on a battered chaise longue. Meanwhile, Ronald and I seated ourselves at a small laminate table in what passed for the drawing room, but was little more than a kitchenette.

Inevitably, before I could produce my papers yet again, a bottle of Teacher's and three glasses materialised. With some misgivings, I passed the now silent courtesan a drink as, much to my relief, Ronald pulled out his Mont Blanc pen and got down to business. After haggling for 20 minutes, I was just starting to get somewhere when our young guest interrupted us.

'I got to go to the bog, and I mean now!'

Ronald was obviously as irritated as I was by the distraction. However, it was patently obvious from Alice's tone that her pressing request should not be ignored.

'Show her the loo for God's sake, Nigel. I told you not to give the creature so much champagne. She is now becoming a pain devoid of sham'.

Deeming it expedient to dignify this feeble pun with a chuckle, I swiftly completed my mission and returned to the business in hand. Thankfully, it was not until I had stowed a remarkably generous quotation in my briefcase that a growling sound, apparently emanating from the direction of the bathroom, became increasingly audible.

Ronald shrugged and said, 'Well, I've done my bit for you, so now get me an order. Meanwhile please go and find out what that wretched woman is up to.'

Finishing my Scotch, I moved down the hall and, as the loo door was ajar, I took the liberty of peeping in. What I beheld was a far from ideal scenario. Alice was snoring like a grampus as she sat bolt upright on the lavatory clutching her drink, having obviously failed to raise her ankle-length velvet dress. Although her namesake in Wonderland had dreamt the pool of tears, this one was for real!

I shot back down the short corridor and grabbed my briefcase.

'OK, everything is fine, I will leave you two turtle doves alone now and grab a cab home. Thanks for the quote. I hope …'

'Wait a minute,' Ronald interrupted as he caught me up at the bathroom door. 'What is going on in there?'

'Alice appears to be recharging her batteries in preparation for your manly onslaught,' I jested, moving rapidly towards the front door.

Unfortunately, there was no way of concealing the obvious.

'This is outrageous. Come back here at once, Nigel.'

Ronald sagged against the wall resignedly. 'You can bugger off right now and take her with you. If you don't, I shall withdraw Gronholm's terms.'

So, five minutes later, there I was stranded at Lancaster Gate in the small hours with an addled and bedraggled young lady. There was no question of leaving her to her own devices as, not only was she highly likely to get run over but also she was a sitting duck for any passing mugger or rapist.

My chivalrous stance was suddenly rewarded when a battered Ford

Cortina clattered to a halt at the kerb nearby and a weasel-faced young man stuck his head out of the driver's window.

'Oi! You two look lost. I shouldn't tout but, if you need a minicab at this late hour, that's me.'

I shouted affirmatively as I steered Alice up to the car.

'Would you please take this young lady home and I will pay you in advance. Oops!'

At that moment my charge's legs buckled and it took all my strength to prevent her falling into the gutter.

Our potential saviour revved his engine threateningly. 'I am not taking her anywhere in that state, mate, unless you accompany her.'

'Done,' I said, as I levered Alice into the Ford's rear seat, confident that she probably dwelt somewhere typical to her calling, like nearby Paddington. We had passed the Royal Lancaster for the third time around the one-way system before I managed to extract this vital piece of intelligence. The good news was that Alice slept like a baby all the way home. The bad news was that our destination was Bishop's Stortford.

By the time that I eventually returned *chez moi* in Fulham it was after 5.30 and my frosties had become more of a blizzard!

Although this narrative depicts a bizarre version of the way business used to be conducted, it does not misrepresent the general modus operandi of the time.

In defence of yesteryear, it should be remembered that the executives who controlled Britain's vital invisible exports were true professionals who made their own decisions. Today, although luxury travel, long lunches and late-night frolics are frowned upon, key industries are obliged to squander funds by employing legions of invasive bureaucrats. Whilst the contribution made by these latter-day insurgents is questionable, the powers that they are given to inhibit their executive superiors are often draconian. Not only do these 'bean counters' impede business efficiency and flexibility but also the ridiculous cost of their superfluous input makes old-style entertainment expenses pale into insignificance.

If the quartermasters had been in charge at Waterloo, we would now all be speaking French!

12

Dangerous Moonlight

In the heady days of courtship before we got married and were blessed with a daughter, Suzie and I travelled abroad whenever possible. As Suzie loved to visit obscure places, I was not at all surprised when she told me that she had booked two weeks in The Gambia as part of our 1993 summer break.

At 200 miles long and 20 miles wide, with a population of fewer than 1 million, this Jack Russell of a nation boldly burrows into mightier Senegal along the banks of the River Gambia. During the Second World War when France's allegiances were questionable, Winston Churchill typically commented upon the little country's strategic status: 'Whatever else happens in Africa, the Empire must hang on to The Gambia at all costs as it is the British finger up the French arsehole!'

For me the trip had an aura of déjà vu as, 34 years earlier, I had served as a Nigerian officer in the Royal West African Frontier Force. The Gambian military was then part of the same colonial army and, even though championing freedom had been one of my duties, Suzie was convinced that I was going to put my foot in it. She was right.

After a jarring landing followed by bumpy deceleration along a thinly tarred strip, the BA Airbus ground to a halt by a dilapidated breeze block building. A flickering neon sign on the rusty metal roof boasted 'Banjul Aerodrome' as a colourful rabble of officials herded us and our fellow passengers into its humid, foetid precincts. Following two hours of chaos, bribery and maddening bureaucracy, we were at last reunited with our luggage and cleared to enter Africa's smallest mainland nation.

Due to my earlier Nigerian experiences, I found the gear-grating taxi ride to our hotel, where we bounced along rutted roads trailing red dust clouds, was very much par for the course. My uninitiated fiancée, however, who was particularly alarmed by the grizzled driver's finely timed negotiation around giant ant hills, was soon wishing that we had opted for Torquay.

Apart from thatch having been largely replaced by corrugated iron, the mud-walled dwellings in the bush villages we passed through were much the same as I remembered them to be in Nigeria. The gratifying aspect of the hour-long journey for me, however, was that the people seemed content and cheerful at a time when horrors were besetting so many other emergent African nations.

The Karaiba Hotel, where we were destined to reside, was well appointed and employed a sufficient surfeit of friendly staff to justify four of its five published stars. We later discovered that the hostelry's survival depended upon a finely tuned financial balancing act. This was between deficits via the obligatory free hosting of government events, versus lucrative subsidies from 'Uncle Sam' for accommodating NASA personnel. Not a lot of people knew it but, at that time, Gambia was the first emergency staging post for USA space shuttle operations.

The configuration and layout of the hotel did convey a slightly disturbing message, however. Whilst the spacious gardens and annexes provided a generous array of sporting and recreational facilities, the whole area was surrounded by razor wire-topped ramparts. In addition to this, all gateways were policed by armed guards, all of which meant that guests were effectively living inside a fortress. Thus, apart from organised excursions, the implication was that anyone venturing outside the precincts of the Karaiba did so at their own risk.

Nevertheless, Suzie and I were having far too much fun to become engrossed in morbid speculation. In fact we frequently wandered onto the public beaches for a swim in the sea and a drink in some of the less sophisticated local bars. Apart from making the day a more interesting, this enabled us to escape from the hotel's inevitable poolside bores.

Our main tormentors here were an egocentric retired US general and a chubby Welsh schoolmaster who looked just like Benny Hill. The former claimed to have wrecked a Middle East conference by telling Yasser Arafat that it was 'better to be a Jew than a fag' and the latter was obsessed with getting me to join the Masons.

It was over lunch on the fifth day that Suzie turned to me and said, 'Darling, why not take a break from the hotel tonight and have dinner at the Marine Club where we had a drink yesterday? Otherwise, we could explore the Banjul nightlife.'

'Let's go for the club,' I replied. 'Banjul is a long way to go on these roads and, although it is the capital, I doubt if it is geared to our kind of revelling.'

'Terrific, it will be fun to have a bit of a change,' Suzie enthused, not in her wildest dreams envisaging what form the change would take.

Our dinner venue was situated a short walk along the beach and, as we departed at 8 p.m., the rear gate sentinels gave us a cheery send-off with flashing smiles and firearms brandishing.

On arrival we were warmly welcomed by the Marine Club's proprietor, Peregrine Drake, an archetypal expat who bulged out of a tatty white ship's captain uniform. Although he wore his gold-braided hat at a jaunty angle above his blue-veined nose, he somehow failed to portray the image of a rugged seafarer. In spite of this, and the fact that his West Country accent was patently bogus, he seemed a decent enough fellow so we accepted his invitation to join him for an aperitif. As 'The Wardroom' was crammed with a motley bunch of barflies and losers from around the world, one free drink was enough. However mine host had other ideas.

'No, please do have the other half; we don't get much passing trade. All the other diners here tonight are residents.'

'So you must be a kind of tropical Fawlty Towers,' said Suzie mischievously. Then, with a touch of canny female suspicion, 'But why would that be?'

Was it my imagination or did I detect a flicker of discomfort pass across Peregrine's sweating face?

'There's not much transport around here so people tend to stay put in the evenings,' was the hesitant reply.

As there were a number of nearby hotels and houses bordering the beach, this did not make much sense, but the subject really did not seem to warrant further debate.

'Let's eat outside in the moonlight,' suggested Suzie.

'A great idea,' I immediately enthused as, due to the still persistent breeze that had disbursed the late afternoon storm clouds, it was worth braving the mosquito threat. So, having downed our second round of margaritas, we adjourned to a table on the club's terrace.

My fiancée was spellbound by her first experience of an African full moon whose magical incandescence ever justifies why so many cultures through the ages have deified this eerie satellite.

Unfortunately, the quality of the setting surpassed that of the cuisine and its fumbling service by an indolent local lad who was incongruously clad in a blue sailor suit and red fez. Fortunately, the excellent wines on offer, although rather pricey, compensated for gastronomic shortcomings. Thus, after settling the tab, we were happy to share Peregrine's penchant for Calvados, after which he bid us a slurred farewell in an accent barely west of Bow Bells.

It was around midnight when we started back along the beach and, as it was still fairly balmy, the subtly reflected lunar light made the gently undulating sea look irresistible. By the time Suzie said, 'Come on, let's go for it,' I was already unbuttoning my shirt. Within seconds, bereft of clothing, inhibitions or any thought of voracious marine creatures, we were both gambolling in the surf like a couple of dolphins. Then, just as we were becoming more romantically inclined, our antics came to an abrupt end when Suzie suddenly stood stock still in the shallows, staring intently back at the beach.

'What's the matter, my love, you almost look serious,' I boomed.

'Shush! I thought that I saw some movement under the trees behind the sand. Just pipe down for a moment,' she urged.

'I am sure it's just your imagination,' I optimistically suggested. 'But as all our gear is on the beach, maybe I had better take a look.'

Running out of the water, it was with a sense of some relief that I found everything strewn around as we had left it. Swiftly grabbing the Nikon from our duffle bag, I rushed back to the water's edge. My timing was perfect and as Suzie, with her modelling attributes still very much intact, emerged like Venus from the waves, I took some frames that would have put David Bailey to shame.

'You rotten devil,' she squealed, as she rushed forward to confiscate the offending camera.

As I laughingly ran backwards, continuing my snapshots, I suddenly collided with a human form. On turning round in great surprise, I was confronted by a small African in uniform who was adjusting his chequered police hat whilst trying not to drop a collection of our effects. Standing behind him was a larger black stranger, clad in the traditional bathrobe and tea cosy garb, who was similarly laden with the remainder of our accessories.

Having snatched my camera, which I was too shocked to retain, the policeman then screamed at me in good English.

'You and your concubine have been under surveillance and I am taking both of you into custody.'

I found my tongue. 'What the hell for?'

'You have broken Gambian and Muslim law by publicly displaying your nakedness and taking obscene pictures.'

I almost laughed. 'Come on, we are hardly offending the general populous,' I remonstrated, quickly checking up on Suzie who was squatting in the sand nearby, covering up at best she could.

Her naked plight brought home to me the stark reality that we were in a weak position to stand on our dignity.

'While we discuss this, please can we have our clothing and possessions back?' I requested in a more respectful tone.

'As you have insulted the Gambian people, you are arrested in shame and will accompany us now, just as you are,' the robed man shouted.

Regardless of the gut-wrenching realisation that we really may have got ourselves into serious hot water, at this last suggestion the red mist descended.

'Listen; you two can parade my body around as much as you like [I was not overweight in those days!] but there is no way that my lady is going anywhere until she is fully clothed. Is that clear?'

Even in the half-light I could tell that my incisiveness had created a moment of indecision, so I swiftly exploited my advantage. Turning to the uniformed policeman, I smiled conspiratorially and steered him a few paces away.

'Listen, officer, I happen to be a London lawyer and I am certain that you chaps must have an on-the-spot cash fine for this kind of situation.'

237

The response was indecently instant. 'Two thousand dalasis.'

I swiftly remembered that, in Africa, credibility demands a haggle. 'Fifteen hundred after all our clothing and effects are returned and I will pay you in cash now.'

The offer equated to about £120 which would have been a local police constable's pay for at least six months. Having briefly jabbered together in their own tongue, our captors agreed to my terms, so everything was returned to us and, within minutes, we were respectable once again.

Now a bargain had been struck, introductions followed and we discovered that we were dealing with Sergeant Cato and his plain-clothes partner, Christopher Amu.

Although I may have gained the initiative, I knew full well that we did not have the agreed sum of money on us. Having gone through the charade of checking and rechecking my wallet and pockets plus Suzie's handbag, I had to bite the bullet.

'Sergeant, I am afraid we only have twelve hundred dalasis with us.' Before outrage could take hold, I swiftly moved on. 'Don't worry, though, we have funds in the Karaiba Hotel's safe so, if you would accompany us to reception, I will pay you the balance.'

After the two of them had had a further brief discussion, the offer was grudgingly accepted. Ironically, our captors' acquiescence dispelled any doubts that I was having over the authenticity of their police status. They had to be bent coppers, otherwise why on earth would they have allowed themselves to be negotiated out of a position in which they held all the cards? As things turned out, I can only assume that their totally illogical behaviour was motivated by the most self-destructive vice of all: avarice.

During our short walk to the Karaiba compound, Christopher fell in silently beside me whilst Sergeant Cato and Suzie followed on behind, apparently conversing amicably. As we passed into the hotel gardens, the gate guards began to surface from their slumbers, a litter of discarded bottles bearing witness to their vigilance!

Having bid them goodnight, we proceeded to the lush spaciousness of the reception area where our police escort strangely faded into the background. Then, as I approached the reception desk to sort out the required funds, an obviously agitated Suzie joined me, her green eyes flashing with outrage.

'Thanks for leaving me with that revolting little swine,' she furiously intoned.

'What, you mean Sergeant Cato? I thought that you two were getting on OK,' I replied; observing that the officer was now skulking behind some large yucca plants whilst his partner was nowhere to be seen.

'Getting on? All he did was to insult me with a string of vile sexual suggestions.'

I was taken aback. 'The bastard. I promise that I will do what I can about that but let's get this bloody fine sorted out first.'

The bell that I was punching eventually summoned a somnolent Audu, the night manager, who informed me that the security vault was locked until 7 a.m. Having explained that only the day staff had access to the deposit boxes, he politely enquired why I needed cash at such a late hour. As I liked Audu, who was a bright, affable young man, I gave him a full and frank synopsis of earlier events which, to my irritation, he seemed to find amusing.

'No, no, sir. These rascals have fooled you, that is not how our law works at all. I should know as I was a policeman until six months ago.'

He peered at Cato through the lobby foliage. 'For a start, he is not wearing proper insignia or sergeant's stripes. I think we should have a word with him and his friend in my office. By the way, where is the other man?'

This mystery was instantly solved as two of the gate guards burst in through the garden terrace swing doors, dragging a dishevelled Christopher Amu between them.

'Good God, Audu, that's him with the security fellows. What the hell is going on around here?' I demanded.

As the trio struggled noisily through the dining area with tables, chairs and cutlery flying in all directions, Audu's answer put another piece of the bizarre jigsaw puzzle in place.

'Unlike the self-appointed sergeant over there, sir, this man I recognise. When I was on the force, he was a regular offender, mainly for violent crime. He is a really nasty guy.'

Before I could respond to this shocking information, a further disturbance occurred.

On observing the plight of his friend, Cato had endeavoured to make a discreet exit via the front entrance. Having failed to deceive the head of security, he started screaming like a banshee as he was prodded back into the foyer by the muzzle of a Sten gun.

There then followed a chaotic gathering of all parties involved in the manager's office which I attended, having sent a tired and still upset Suzie to bed. After half an hour of everyone yelling at each other and down the telephone to the local constabulary, a clearer situation emerged. Amu was, indeed, a crook by the name of Boka Igbo, in cahoots with Constable John Ezenago who had masqueraded as Sergeant Cato, one of his superior officers. Neither of them had had any right to detain Suzie and me, let alone demand money. There was a police contingent on its way to arrest both of them and I was requested over the phone by a station officer to prepare a statement of events by the morning.

My most voluble contribution to the proceedings was venting my

240

spleen on the dissembling couple, particularly Ezenago for upsetting Suzie with his prurient innuendo. Then, feeling fatigued and without my 1,200 dalasis which, having been found Igbo's pocket was being retained as evidence, I retired to bed for what was left of the night.

At 8 a.m. the following morning sunlight lanced painfully into my half-open eyes as a persistent tapping slowly stirred me from a deep sleep.

'Someone failed to draw the curtains,' muttered Suzie as she surfaced to join me in reluctant wakefulness.

I swiftly donned a robe and opened our room door to reveal the Karaiba's senior concierge, Nelson, who was noticeably failing to live up to his usual ebullient image.

'So sorry to disturb you Mr Kemble-Clarkson but are the two of you ready to report to the police station with your statements covering last night's unfortunate happenings?'

'You can count me out, for a start,' said a voice from behind me.

Our uncomfortable visitor coughed nervously. 'As the local police seem to lack motor transport, the hotel car will convey you to their station in Cololi for the trial of the criminal constable. The journey takes twenty minutes and the case will be heard at nine a.m.'

I was in no mood to be chivvied. 'We are not ready to go anywhere. Thanks to you, we have just woken up, our statements have not been prepared and we have as yet to bathe and have breakfast. The police will have to wait.'

Before Nelson had a heart attack, I agreed to write out a résumé of events as quickly as I could over breakfast. This would then have to be countersigned by Suzie, as she had no desire for further involvement, after which I would be free to assist the police.

Ere departing, I bid Suzie a reluctant farewell as she settled by the main pool, attracting keen attention from some master race hunks that were part of a Lufthansa stand-by crew. Then, just before 9.30, I was en route to bear witness in the hotel's Ford Galaxy which was driven by a Senegalese called Hassan.

The driver and I chatted amiably as we bumped along a gravel track which eventually led to a primitive township on the edge of some dense woodland. Here, our final destination turned out to be a large, thatch roofed, wooden bungalow with an elevated porch and

241

veranda reminiscent of a Hollywood Western. Hanging on rusty chains over the main door was a battered sign boasting 'COLOLI PO...ICE' in faded gold lettering.

On alighting from the car, I was instantly plunged into the hive of activity which surrounded the building, making it appear more like a recreation centre than a police station. Whilst squawking chickens, naked children and barking dogs rushed about in all directions, several unkempt policemen laughed and openly flirted with the local talent. Many of these colourfully robed and turbaned ladies wore gaudy face make-up which, as I recalled from my Nigerian days, denoted the world's oldest profession.

As I stood bemusedly in the midst of this turmoil, I was accosted by a gaunt Irishman in a soiled white cassock as he tottered down the porch steps cursing like a trooper.

'Hey, you, the bastards locked me up again. I had to cough up half the Sunday offertory in bribes just because some bloody idiot tries to enter Heaven by stepping under my motor. Said I'd been drinking. The very cheek of it, to be sure.'

Although this was obviously a priest from some local Jesuit mission, the breath that wafted in my direction would have stripped the paint off the Sistine Chapel. When I failed to respond, he spat a gob of phlegm at my feet and snarled, 'Heretics and heathens, the lot of them.'

Then, having lowered himself into a battered Volkswagen Beetle he clattered off in a cloud of red dust, more like a demon than an emissary of the Lord. Whilst I was musing on this bizarre event, an immaculate police corporal with a white lanyard round his shoulder suddenly stamped to attention in front of me.

'Mr Kemble-Clarkson to see the Commandant?'

'That's correct,' I replied.

'ADC Sampson. Please come with me.'

'What about the car? It is on loan from the Karaiba Hotel?'

'I suggest that you hang on to it, sir. There is no police transport except bicycles and your driver can wait out here.'

The Corporal's suggestion obviously delighted Hassan, who had already been eyeing up some potential female targets.

'See you soon. Try not to drink too much beer,' I called to him as

242

I followed my guide into the cop shop's inner sanctum, preceded by a couple of confused hens.

I was initially led through the main reception area, where a harassed sergeant was doing his best to sort out a babbling cross-section of the community. We then passed down a corridor, at the end of which was a door marked 'Commandant'. After a cursory rap on the panelling, the ADC preceded me into a large, stuffy office, lined with rusty filing cabinets and poorly illuminated via grubby frosted windows. Behind an oversized metal desk, on which an anti-quated electric fan gently riffled an assortment of forms and papers, slouched the corpulent mainspring of local law and order.

During Sampson's introduction, Major Botombi's chestfull of medals clinked together as he strained to separate his ample backside from a worn leather armchair. In spite of the sweat stains on his blue uniform, his decorations and the gleaming black Sam Browne indicated that he was taking the forthcoming proceedings seriously. He was obviously far from happy with me, however.

'I apologise for the gross offence you have suffered at the hands of a renegade policeman, but you are very late!'

Saying nothing, I passed him my statement, which he snatched rudely.

'Let me study this thoroughly so that we can get this matter sorted out in the correct manner. You may sit in that cane chair; it is probably the most comfortable one.'

Twenty minutes later I was regretting my earlier refusal of a warm Carlsberg as I completed my third count of insect carcases affixed to a foetid flypaper suspended overhead. At last the Major concluded his ponderous perusal of the three-page résumé and, pointedly ignoring me, turned to his ADC.

'Have the prisoner brought in at once, Corporal.'

As Sampson marched away, I decided that it was time to mark my territory.

'How much longer have I got to sit around in your dump of a police station, Major? I want to get back to my holiday, chop chop.'

Botomby regarded me malevolently as he dabbed his perspiring ape-like features with a grubby yellow handkerchief. I knew that he was dying to say that it was my stupidity that had landed me there –

which was totally true – but he wisely avoided the temptation. Instead, he slowly donned and adjusted a gilded peaked hat as if to emphasise his importance.

'I am sure, Mr Kemble-Clarkson, that you want to see justice done as much as I do. And kindly address me as Commandant,' he growled.

Fortunately, further dialogue was forestalled by the noisy arrival of Constable Ezenagu preceded by an armed guard with Corporal Sampson bringing up the rear calling 'Left, right, left, right' at an unmarchable pace. They then deafeningly stamped a halt and left turn prior to the escort crashing his rifle from shoulder to floor in three clockwork movements.

As the Gambian Police force was run entirely on military lines, internal justice was meted out arbitrarily and so the ensuing proceedings were mercifully brief. The 15-minute hearing was conducted in the local tongue except when I was required to identify the prisoner, who managed to avoid my gaze for the duration.

It was after the accused had been sentenced and propelled from the office looking very sorry for himself, that I managed my old trick of opening my mouth and putting my foot in it!

After the noisy retinue had departed, Major Botomby sat back and actually managed a sadistic smile.

'Well, that's the end of that idiot's police career.'

I extricated myself from the bum-numbing bamboo chair. 'Well done, Commandant. If you would be kind enough to return my money, I will be on my way. Incidentally, what happens to the other chap, will he get hard labour too?'

Holding out his podgy hand to say goodbye, Botomby replied, 'He has to go before the civil courts and I believe …' Suddenly his eyes narrowed cannily. 'Wait a minute, how did you know that Ezenago's discharge included a period of hard labour?'

'Because, during sentencing, I heard you say IHL. I remember, from taking company orders when I was serving in Nigeria many years ago, that this means intensive hard labour.' Foot in!

With amazing agility for his bulk, the Commandant was on his feet in a trice. 'You were in the Nigerian Army?' he demanded with his eyes like saucers.

'I was, over thirty years ago when it was still a British colonial force. I would love to chat with you about it sometime but I really must be getting back to my fiancée who …'

I was interrupted excitedly. 'And you were a company commander?'

'Yes, only briefly due to a shortage of …'

Again I was not allowed to finish. 'Once an officer, always an officer, Captain Kemble-Clarkson. This puts a whole new complexion on this disgraceful situation.'

Much to my surprise, the police chief threw me a half-smart salute then clasped my hand in his sweating paw. 'Excuse me, Captain. I must use the telephone immediately.'

As he commenced dialling, I observed, to my consternation, that the statement, with dalasis attached, was furtively slipped into a battered attaché case on the desk.

In hindsight, I should have appreciated that, from little Gambia's standpoint, Nigeria was a revered and feared West African superpower. Also, as I later discovered, a majority of the Gambian officer and senior NCO cadre were trained at Nigerian military academies.

Botombi's phone conversation did not take long. Having submitted some form of report in Gambian, the response inspired his rapt attention as if he was receiving a reissuing of the Ten Commandments. When the call ended, the Commandant positively beamed at me with stars in his eyes.

'I have just spoken with the DG himself and, in view of your important military past, he insists that you attend his personal rehearing of the Ezenago case. As this is to take place at Banjul Police HQ as soon as possible, we must move at once.'

'Hang on a moment, Commandant. I have just made it crystal clear that I wish to return to the Karaiba immediately. The case is over so far as I am concerned but, if you fellows want a retrial, you may use my statement.'

Wringing his hands in quivering panic, Botombi played his sympathy card convincingly. 'But the DG wants to meet you personally and if you refuse to accompany me, I am finished.'

Having always been a sucker for a hard-luck story, I caved in. 'In for a penny, in for a pound; I will attend, but firstly, who or what is the DG and secondly, how do we travel twenty miles to Banjul with no police transport?'

Almost crying with relief, the Commandant quickly regained his composure. 'Your first answer is, Director General Fraser, chief of The Gambia's military and security services. Secondly, as our police Land Rover has been stolen, I must requisition your hotel car.'

Uncharitably thinking to myself, more likely sold off than stolen, I replied, 'You square that up with the Karaiba, then I will use your phone to put my fiancée in the picture and we are on our way.'

With Botombi and Corporal Sampson shouting orders in the background, I eventually got through to Suzie at the pool and tried to explain the unbelievable. As usual, she was philosophical.

'Well, at least you can see if the capital is worth a visit. Do hurry back as soon as you can though, darling. Jorgen and Hans are becoming very tedious company.'

'You keep it that way. Love you.'

I hung up, determined to extricate myself as soon as possible from the absurd tide of events into which I seemed have immersed myself.

How do you get a 6-foot armed guard, a struggling prisoner and a 20-stone police chief into the back of a Ford car? With extreme difficulty, is the answer. I should know, as I created the situation by flatly refusing to give up my front passenger seat when Ezenago was dragged to the car in handcuffs from the constabulary's side door. The prisoner was patently dreading his ordeal in Banjul and his battered, bedraggled state was such that, if he had not grossly offended Suzie, I might have interceded. Anyway, whilst he was being settled into the rear seat, with the Commandant reluctantly squeezing in beside him, the guard was having a severe problem with shipping his rifle.

'For God's sake try unfixing your bayonet,' I suggested in exasperation.

When this was followed up by a lambasting from Botombi, the flustered constable got out of the car to sort out his blade, leaving his door open. In a trice Ezenago seized his moment but, echoing his stupidity of the night before on the beach, instead of plunging into the nearby wood, he fled across open ground.

The Commandant screamed at Hassan who, with the rear door flapping and leaving the guard behind, accelerated off in hot pursuit. Not to be left out of the fun, a mob of villagers streamed along beside us in full cry, joining in the spirit of the chase as our car bounced crazily over cassava patches. The fugitive never really stood a chance and, when a brindled mongrel fastened on to his trouser leg, he gave up.

On our arrival moments later, having miraculously avoided breaking an axle, Ezenago could not wait to seek refuge in the Ford from the crowd's rough handling. When the police escort rejoined us he received another earful from his boss, after which we were, at last, off to see the Wizard.

Apart from a 5-mile stretch of dual carriageway with real tarmacadam, there were no further surprises on our journey to the capital. Conversation was minimal en route apart from the prisoner's pathetic pleadings for mercy, but he was swiftly silenced on each occasion by a blow from his guard.

When we finally arrived in Banjul, the town was somewhat of a disappointment. Although breeze block housing was in evidence, the only substantial buildings were run-down relics from the colonial era. Any ground not built on was occupied by shanty town shacks and ship container homes, whilst shopping outlets differed little from rural marketplaces.

Even though there was a proliferation of cyclists and livestock on the streets, motor traffic was light, so Hassan was able to dodge and bully his way through to our destination with comparative ease. Our stalwart chauffeur was the only person in the car who was having a good day, and I was certain that he knew exactly where to access whatever pleasures Banjul had to offer.

Police Headquarters occupied a majestic three-storey stone edifice whose crumbling decorative scrolls and escutcheons suggested that it had once housed the courts of justice. Having dropped off the prisoner and escort at the 'CH...RGE RO...M', we drove round to the front of the building where a white marble staircase curved up to a pillared entrance.

It was instantly apparent as we alighted from our transport that the gallant Major had omitted to take his ego-blockers again. Having adjusted his crumpled uniform, he turned his back on me and shouted something at a sentry in red and blue livery who had just made a reasonable job of presenting arms.

I winked at Hassan and said, 'Off you go and enjoy yourself but please make sure that you are back here in an hour's time and I will make it worth your while.'

Whilst the chauffeur drove off happily, I followed Botombi who was waiting breathlessly halfway up the stairs with our colourfully attired guide. We then continued our ascent and passed through the main door into a lofty reception area. Here our ears were instantly assailed by a deafening cacophony which only a concentration of God's creatures can engender.

As the crowd scene extras virtually duplicated those that we had just left behind, it almost seemed as if the Wizard had transported Cololi's entire chorus there ahead of us! However, the distribution of roles had varied somewhat in that the shady lady quota was up on a sorely depleted chicken count. This swapping fowl for foul (geddit?) was balanced somewhat by the presence of two flask-swigging friars and a plump, lascivious-looking nun.

Having enthusiastically carved a passage through the throng with his rifle butt, our escort ushered us through a heavily guarded door which opened into a comfortably furnished anteroom. Here we encountered a much-decorated, grizzled officer in olive green field dress who, in spite of his apparent age, lithely bounced from behind a stout oak desk to greet us. As my portentous companion was seriously starting to get on my nerves, I brushed him aside and, stepping forward, held out my hand.

'Director General Fraser, I presume?'

'No, I am merely his ADC, Brigadier General Arthur Unegbi. Most honoured to meet you Captain Kemble-Clarkson. Please make yourself comfortable on the sofa; I will join you in a moment.'

He then turned to Botombi and appeared to ask him a series of questions in the local tongue. It was very apparent from the increasing crescendo of the exchange, and the wilting demeanour of the Major, that some inadequate answers were being offered. The Brigadier then abruptly concluded in English with an incisive, 'So sort it out now.'

As the object of his wrath slouched dejectedly from the room, Unegbi poured us both a gin and tonic and sat down in a leather armchair beside me.

'The man is not only a total idiot but also a thief. So you travelled here from Cololi in civilian transport?'

'Yes, the Karaiba Hotel's Ford Galaxy,' I replied.

'If Botombi had not mislaid his allocated long wheelbase Land Rover – which I intend to fully investigate – there would have been room for the two buglers who were to have accompanied you. This has now caused an inconvenient delay whilst he returns to Cololi in one of our Jeeps which will then have to bring them back here.'

I was confused. 'But what have buglers got to do with my meeting with the DG?'

'General Fraser would not dream of holding a hearing without discharging the full honours due to a Nigerian officer.'

Observing my incredulous expression, he went on, 'I know that you probably find this rather over the top but our DG does love, what you call, standing on ceremony.'

I opted not to ask why Banjul was bereft of buglers and pursued a diplomatic course of complicity whilst we awaited the brass section. Having consumed a surprisingly tasty chicken salad which was served with some local beer to wash it down, I decided to relax and observe my host performing his duties.

Once he was back behind his football pitch of a bureau, the brigadier proceeded to field a stream of loquacious delegations, most of which required his signature on one document or another. However, due to the diversity of their uniforms, it was impossible to determine which branch of the police or armed services the visitors represented. In fact, the colourful variety of outfits displayed would have done credit to a Third Reich cocktail party or an amateur production of *The Student Prince*! During a lull in activities, my curiosity got the better of me so I decided to re-establish the old platitude that 'no question is indiscreet; only the answer'.

'What's with all the different uniforms, Brigadier?' I enquired. 'The Gambia must have a very complicated administration.'

'Corruption, Captain Kemble-Clarkson,' was the surprising response. 'The regime that replaced your country's occupation a few years ago is in chaos, particularly the Ministry of War and Defence. A number of its more wayward administrators individually accepted bribes for awarding army and police force clothing contracts to four separate Asian textile firms. As a result, we now have an enormous surplus of uniforms in different styles and colours which have to be used up.'

The explanation defied further comment, so I borrowed Unegbi's phone to touch base with Suzie. I had just completed the call when there was a particularly urgent knocking on the office's side door. At the ADC's bidding, a junior police officer marched into the room, saluted smartly, and made a short announcement. I did not have to speak the lingo to know that the time had at last arrived to meet the wonderful Wizard of Oz!

Feeling somewhat exposed in shorts, sandals and a yellow T-shirt with Daffy Duck on the pocket, I followed the Brigadier into a spacious, flagstoned hall. To my relief, amongst the dozen or so militiamen who were brushing, polishing and checking each other's scarlet and green uniforms, two of them were buffing bugles.

Suddenly a pair of gilded white doors at the far end of the chamber swung open to admit an enormous Asian sergeant major. As he stomped in, his very presence froze everyone into silence, including the ADC. Nevertheless, Sikh hero or not, in his flamboyant regalia and royal blue turban, he instantly reminded me of the Indian doorman at L'Hirondelle, a popular London bordello just off Piccadilly.

A series of martial barks inspired the rapid formation of two parallel green and red files which lined the route to the ornate doorway. Whilst bugles blared and arms were presented, I preceded Brigadier Unegbi through the gauntlet. As the Sergeant Major saluted crisply, my long-awaited host emerged from the portal to greet me.

The DG appeared to be around 40 years old and was an impressive sight to behold. His tall athletic frame was clad in an exquisitely tailored white uniform, adorned with a light blue silk sash and a glistening display of stars and medals. On my approach his fine blue-black features broke into a dazzling smile as he stepped forward and gripped my hand.

'General Fraser at your service, Captain Kemble-Clarkson,' he drawled in the affected tones of a 1950s BBC newscaster. 'Welcome to my humble lair. Do come on in. You too, Unegbi.'

As we entered a spacious office, the sudden drop in temperature and humidity boasted the very latest in air conditioning technology. To compliment the room's robust antique furnishings, the walls were hung with fine paintings of historic battles and military figures, including Wellington and Marlborough. The focal mural adornment, however, was a crossed pair of gold-mounted cavalry sabres suspended over the obvious throne of authority.

The Brigadier and I were soon seated in comfortable armchairs as glasses of cold white wine were served by an ageing liveried flunky wearing the inevitable scarlet fez. Meanwhile, before settling behind his Louis XIV writing table which was situated on a raised dais, the DG passed me my statement and dalasis.

'I don't think that we shall need those any more,' he intoned ingratiatingly. Then, totally out of the blue, 'I bet that you have never heard of the Fraser tribe, eh?'

'Not that I recall,' I cautiously responded.

'Have you read any Flashman novels?'

Fortunately, I was an avid fan. 'I have read and possess all of them. Of course: you share your name with the author, George Macdonald Fraser.'

The General chuckled conspiratorially. 'Before going for officer training in your country, a colonial subaltern insisted that the most amusing way to study Victorian military history was to read the Flashman Papers. He was right and I loved every book so, as I hated my Gambian name, Botato, I changed it to that of the great author.'

As I smiled politely, he abruptly altered the direction of the conversation in the typical fashion of those who are accustomed to calling the shots.

'So when were you at Sandhurst?'

'I wasn't, I was at Mons Officer Cadet School in the fifties.'

'Goodness me, I was there too, but not until the eighties. Bloody awful town Aldershot, what?'

'Ghastly,' I agreed. 'But Guildford has some good pubs and

London is only a short drive away.'

Fraser gave a nostalgic sigh. 'Indeed, I remember that the Angel in Guildford was a great place to meet the ladies. In London, my favourite watering hole was the Duke of Wellington in Eaton Terrace ...'

With the ADC looking increasingly bored, we reminisced for a while and I must admit that Fraser's mercurial charm, so often found in demagogues, was pleasantly infectious. Then, all of a sudden, he did it again. Fixing me with an intense stare, he completely changed the subject.

'So, what have you got to say about Nigeria?'

Sensing a loaded question, I started to waffle about my time spent there, extolling the virtues of the early independent leaders such as Gowon and Ironsi. I was soon cut short.

'Captain, I am talking about your view of Nigeria today.'

Although I considered the country to be seriously out of control, as I was facing a psychopath, I decided upon a course of discretion.

'A nation of great stature and ongoing potential, sir, but I was very upset over the Biafran War debacle when far too many good Nigerians were slaughtered.'

Much to my chagrin, the General rose slowly to his feet, his black face seeming to turn even darker with anger, as his red-veined eyes bulged.

'You Brits make me laugh. You seem to believe that armed aggression, which made your country so great and powerful, is a white man's preserve. Look at Flashman's imperial world, one bloody war after another.'

I diplomatically refrained from pointing out that our greatest secret of success lay in confining confrontations to away matches. We had learned this lesson in 1066 when our last international home fixture had proved somewhat of a disaster.

However, as I was musing on how best to avoid dropping a further clanger, my host had another mood swing and broke into fits of mirth, swiftly echoed by the Brigadier. Was it me, or were things becoming a tad paranoid?

After the DG had recovered his composure he sat down again and beamed at me mischievously.

'Only joking, my friend. Let's cull some vermin.'

What then followed was simply a more dramatic version of the Coroli hearing. What I did find slightly odd, though, was that, as the prisoner was marched into the office, the buglers sounded a long 'G' on their instruments. In my experience, this was normally the signal used on a rifle range to warn the butt team that shooting was about to commence!

As a tearful Ezenago was marched away with his dishonourable discharge confirmed, but the hard labour sentence reduced from six to three months at my request.

Fraser turned to me. 'Do have another glass of wine. I want a private word in your ear.'

Having bid farewell to Unegbi, I sat down again and accepted the drink.

'OK, fire ahead General but, with great respect, I must not be too long. My driver has been hanging around for two hours and I really must get back to my fiancée as soon as possible.'

'To hell with your driver. But your good lady is vitally important so I will be brief.'

The paternal role now kicked in. 'To be perfectly frank Captain Kemble-Clarkson, I have to say that, for a man who has lived in West Africa, I find your conduct on the beach last night naive, if not downright irresponsible.'

As this criticism was totally justified, I gave a contrite nod.

The DG then continued his reprimand more intensely. 'It may interest you to know that only three weeks ago, very near to where you were taking a dip, two English air hostesses were beaten half to death, then raped. Also, a week earlier in the same vicinity, a Swedish doctor was shot dead whilst walking his dog.'

I was suitably taken aback, but as I started to express horror at this disturbing information, General Fraser leaned across his desk and gripped my arm.

'Listen, Captain, the Gambian Police are corrupt scum and the useless government, which has been in power ever since you chaps handed over, does nothing about it. However, you can rest assured that, within a very short time, I and certain of my compatriots will be taking remedial action.'

And so it came to pass that dangerous moonlight enabled me to meet the prime mover responsible for Gambia's military coup the following year.